A beginner's ultimate guide to transitioning to a plant-based diet and to navigating the social aspects of a vegan lifestyle

lettuce live better

ASSILE BEYDOUN

Publishing information
Publishing, design, and production facilitated by Passionpreneur Publishing, A division of
Passionpreneur Organization Pty Ltd, ABN: 48640637529

www.PassionpreneurPublishing.com
Melbourne, VIC | Australia

CONTENTS

To Jude

May you lead a generation that grows up to rebuild faster than ours destroyed, and may you do it with courage and compassion. Stay happy, stay kind, and forever fight the good fight.

This book would not have been possible without:

Ata, who was the reason I started writing this book. He believed in me so much until I had to start believing in myself. And Roupen, who was the reason I completed it. He reminded me every day that I am enough to make a difference.

Maher, who was patient as I evolved, supportive when I spent weekends writing, and endured our fridge transformation. And Jude, who is the reason I fight for this planet, which is all going to be his one day.

Mom and Dad, who taught me to always fight for what I believe in, and Hassan and Rawan, the first vegetarians I ever knew who had to deal with "Where do you get your protein from?" at family dinner tables way before I did.

Dalia, who is the reason I fell in love with writing as a kid when we spent our mornings on tree branches reciting poetry and my teachers, Megan Khairallah and the late Alexander Ammerman, who taught me that words have the power to drive change.

Karl, who taught me to be real, raw, and true to myself, and Toni, who always believed in my crazy ideas and helped me bring them to life.

Gaby, Nadia, Heba, Fabiana and Nicole who have watched me embrace this journey, cheered me on, and taught me that true friends can grow separately without growing apart.

Hiba and new friends I met in Bali, who played a major role in my spiritual journey.

Gulper and the friends I made through the Dubai Vegan Community, who do this for the animals and who remind me every day what compassion looks like on a dinner plate.

Ghady, Nada, Grace, Rana, Andy, Roula, Rima, Nour, Georges, Razan, and so many other very close friends and family members, who always cared, heard me rant, watched me grow, and reminded me every day that I need to keep going.

Seb, who told me that there are different kinds of activists and that I am right where I need to be to truly make a difference.

And Moustafa, who said, "People need to hear your story. When will you write your book?"

Thank you for supporting a great cause.

You are making a difference! All proceeds from this book are being donated to build Palemahan Animal Rescue Sanctuary in Uluwatu. This has been a long-term passion project, and a generous friend has agreed to donate the land if we can raise enough to shelter and feed rescued farm animals. Thank you for being part of this.

CHAPTER 1

THE VERY VEGANING

How my relationship with food transformed my life

Every time you eat or drink, you are either feeding disease or fighting it.

—HEATHER MORGAN

I was a very average kid.

I had average hair, average eyes, average grades, and an average family with an average income. Nothing about my childhood seemed extraordinary. If anything, it was filled with more shortcomings than triumphs. But what I didn't know back then is that you don't really need anything above average to lead an extraordinary life—a life that is fueled by purpose, that drives true change—so you may leave this world better than how you found it.

I grew up in a war-torn city; we led simple lives. I had older cousins—whom my family rooted for and called "doctor," in hopes that they'd "make it" in life—and younger ones who required attention and care. I was safely sandwiched in the middle of the family bustle—well fed, sent to a good school, and seldom patted on the back. I didn't have any attention-worthy talent or a worrying bad habit. I wasn't nicknamed or glorified or celebrated. I was the average child that blended into the many colors of a large family, and I often felt that my disappearance would go unnoticed. Just as I disappeared into the dim corners at my grandma's house, I also did so at school. I was unquestionably a misfit. When other teenagers were plotting hookups and parties, I spent afternoons on the library floor reading *Macbeth*, writing sonnets, and contemplating our existence. I befriended my teachers because other students seemed too simple-minded. Somehow, I would force myself to be the odd one out. On some level, I thought that conforming meant surrendering to the mediocrity of my existence. What a terrible thought that was—to die average.

When I turned twenty, I yearned for adventure. I needed more meaning. I left home, moved to Dubai, and found a great corporate job. I got married, made new friends, afforded fancy dinners, baked cupcakes for the office, and planned birthday parties and baby showers. In my free time, I binge-watched more Netflix shows than I can now recall, barbecued burgers on the terrace, basted turkeys for Thanksgiving, and traveled around Europe whenever I got a chance.

I constantly asked myself, "Is my life finally starting to become a bit more meaningful?"

I had what most people dreamt of: a kind and loving husband, a perfectly polite baby boy, a charming house with a fence and a pool, and a great career in a *Fortune* 500 company.

But I wasn't happy.

In an era where everyone struggles to fit in, leading an average, comfortable life sounded perfect. So why wasn't it enough?

Ten years of Dubai's famous Friday brunches and homemade fudge brownies had left me overweight. My pant size moved up as gradually as the rising temperatures of the country's scorching summers, and my body completely changed after pregnancy. I had anemia, my hair was falling out, and I had irritable bowel syndrome. After early-morning day care drop-offs and long days running a multimillion-dollar business with so much passion, like it was my own, I was also pretty much exhausted by 6:00 p.m. I would get home, crash on the couch, put my legs up on the coffee table, literally rest a bowl of chips on my belly for the perfect snacking-while-lying-down experience, and watch whatever was on the TV screen at that very moment (oftentimes it was *Mickey Mouse Clubhouse*, the news, or a black screen) because who has the energy to reach out for the TV remote after such a long day?

Of course, I tried every diet out there. I tried diets that tell you to live on meat and butter because somehow it made sense that cholesterol and clogged arteries would lead to the perfect body. I picked up any magazine with a less-than-thirty days to a bikini body promise on the cover and bought dodgy herbal slimming teas with labels in Chinese letters I couldn't understand. Nothing worked. My energy was always low, and for every kilogram I lost, I gained two. Nothing made me look good, and nothing made me feel good either.

The one thing that was failing me faster than my body was my mind.

While the world was posting elevator selfies on Instagram, I hated taking pictures. Most days, I looked in the mirror and didn't really recognize myself. I would have thought my rock bottom came on a Saturday afternoon on the floor of an H&M dressing room, when I was drenched in self-loathing and shamelessly sobbing while trying to pull up a skirt, but it got worse.

One day, when I was home for the holidays, I found my old journal. It had a list of my life goals, and as the number-one ambition, what a sixteen-year-old me had written was a naive but raw and honest Miss Universe pageant statement: "Create World Peace." I felt so far off from the adult I had always dreamt of becoming. I was nowhere close to making the world a better place, and I struggled to figure out my purpose or answer why I existed. The next morning, I received news that a colleague of mine had passed away in a car accident. From that moment, my world became darker. I was haunted by thoughts of death and began wondering if existing without a real purpose even mattered at all.

It got so bad that my closest friend recommended I get professional help. I saw a psychiatrist and was medically diagnosed with depression, generalized anxiety disorder and post-traumatic stress disorder (PTSD) from a childhood trauma. I ran out of the clinic in complete shock. A professional had just labeled me with a bunch of diseases. Was I *sick*? Remember when I thought my dressing room breakdown was my rock bottom? Oh no! Rock bottom was sitting in my car, in the scorching heat of the desert's summer days, for two hours outside the doctor's office, crying over a prescription for Zoloft.

As the heat started rising around noon and it was becoming unbearable to stay within the car with the engine still off, I thought about how I could have ended up here. All this time, I had thought I was on a quest for "world peace," while my own spirit was at war. I didn't know much in that very instant, but I knew I needed an answer and that an antidepressant wasn't one. If I was going to fight this, I first needed to figure out what the battle was about, so I decided to strip myself back to my very core. I found a fasting retreat and spent eight days in the tropics alone, consuming nothing but green juices and raw coconut water.

A week of no food for an emotional eater seemed impossible, but, by the third day, all I was hungry for was my return to nature. I was craving answers more than any meal. I spent time with myself. I learned about the healing power of raw foods and the universe's different energies. It was a turning point, not only because it changed my relationship with food (realizing you can live a week without eating reshapes how you look at French fries) but also because it changed my relationship with the universe.

During my first week attempting to "integrate" back into society after my fast, I was invited to a barbecue for twenty people. I sat right in front of a giant grill crammed with hot dogs, beef ribs, chicken thighs, lamb shanks, and, of course, as I was in the Middle East, shish taouk. The different smells made me think about the different animals on there. Were we about to eat chicken with a side of cow? Was their life so meaningless that we even commoditize their death? How can we live in peace when we cause so much harm? Is a life not worth more than a sandwich?

Fresh back from experiencing the healing power of what nature grew from its roots made me question everything about our food choices.

These choices have been normalized for so long that they have become our culture—a culture that has been accepted for so long that it is now a tradition. But traditions do not justify morality, nor do they exemplify all that is right. I thought about all the "okay" things humanity has gone through that are no longer okay at all. Women as second-class citizens, slavery and female circumcision . . . all these were accepted earlier. At one point not long ago, some doctors were recommending smoking for stress relief. And we evolved. We equipped ourselves with knowledge, science, and compassion to stand up against such traditions. And even though new ideologies were resisted when something had become a norm, it was only a matter of time before the world saw it for what it was: unjustified and unnecessary.

Some people describe this realization as everything they know tumbling down into rubble; for me, it was an explosion of everything I did not know manifesting before my eyes. I ran away to learn about what is "natural," but there was nothing natural about how we were eating. No animal in nature drinks the milk of another species or drinks milk after infancy. There was nothing natural about the fact that, according to the Centers for Disease Control and Prevention (CDC), seven out of the ten leading causes of death in the United States today are related to food and lifestyle. Or about the fact that I would choose to eat a goat but pet my dog.

Once I figured out how to eat right, I started to feel my body change. I had more energy, I lost a lot of weight, and I was glowing. My body was transforming before my eyes. At thirty, I looked better than I did as a teenager. Nine months later, I ran blood work, as I often did due to my anemia, and, to my doctor's surprise and mine, my iron levels were perfect. I hadn't been taking any supplements other than what nature intended, and here I was—living proof of the power of dark greens.

I had become fascinated with the power of plants. I got a certification in plant-based nutrition from eCornell and the T. Colin Campbell Center for Nutrition Studies. I was moderating juice fasts and reading about mindfulness. I had the energy to work out every day. I started a ten-day exercise challenge that turned into thirty days, and then a year. I was at my best, and there was a world of knowledge I was fervently consuming. A pressing voice in my head kept telling me to take the intensity of my emotions and do something with it. I started the Dubai Vegan Community to spread awareness but also to meet like-minded people. I held talks, events, and meetups. When I received messages every single day from people saying, "Thank you for helping us belong," or "This has been the best decision I have ever made. Thank you," I realized this was no longer about me. I was helping people eat better and understand what the word "vegan" really means. I found myself investing hours showing them how to read labels and how to shop for and cook basic meals. I was watching them heal. The prescription I had in my hand that day in the doctor's carpark was to treat a symptom, as all medicine does, but modern medicine doesn't tell us how to help prevent disease which, at its essence, can be done by learning how to just eat clean.

It wasn't only other people's health on the line here. Eating a plant-based diet is one of the best ways to reduce a single individual's environmental impact and help combat climate change. Researchers at the University of Oxford found that cutting meat and dairy products from a diet and eating local plant-based food could reduce a person's carbon footprint from food by up to 73 percent. But most importantly, I was also helping prevent the suffering of other sentient beings. Perhaps my previous "comfortable" life hadn't felt so comfortable because it was coming at a cost, the cost of so many animal lives taken.

Several years, ten kilograms, and six hundred bowls of hummus later, I finally knew how I was going to be ticking off sixteen-year-old me's ambition bucket list. I was playing my part and helping one person at a time transition. On average, every person going vegan for one year saves as much water as 23,617 quick showers, as much forest land as two football fields, as much CO_2 emissions as using a car for more than a year, and an average of three hundred animal lives. Ah, world peace!

Vegan For

The animals	Our water	World hunger
The rainforests	Compassion	Wildlife
Our health	Peace	Our planet

You must have picked this book up because you are a seeker yourself. If you are seeking answers, solutions or information, then you have landed on the right page. Together, throughout this book, we will work on a transition to a plant-based diet so that you can better fuel your body and live with the peace of mind of leading a vegan lifestyle.

CHAPTER 2

YOU ARE WHAT YOU EAT

Don't be a rotting corpse

Let's face it; our current lifestyle is killing us.

We are more obese than we have ever been, we are dying of heart disease, diabetes and cancers, and we live on pills and medical care bills. Autoimmune disease rates are higher than ever, and sometimes, we visit doctors for the following conditions as often as we visit our grandmas:

Heart Disease
Diabetes
Stroke
High Cholesterol
Cancer
Kidney Failure
Heart Attack
High Blood Pressure
Osteoporosis
Obesity

WHAT'S GOING ON?

In a way, we're all slacking with our health.

We often forget that our health is ours to preserve. We decide what happens next with every meal we eat and with every piece of fruit or buttery cookie we choose. But the magnitude of that decision has been diminished by this great medical system that we have today, one that we can rely on to take care of us and our bodies, no matter what happens. There seems to be a magic fix for every disease, a pill for every pain, and a surgery for every issue. But while we are all grateful for the great doctors who save our lives every day, why are we needing them more and more? Because medicine and the medical system is there to cure disease, not to prevent it. We have been taking prevention for granted, so when will we start working on healthier versions of ourselves instead?

In this chapter, we will explore why we need to fix our food habits and how our current diet is making us sick. We will discuss a paradigm shift that helps us question some of the nutrition myths we have been taking for granted, including:

- Do we really need to eat animal protein to be healthy and build muscles?
- Do we need milk for calcium?
- Are we naturally meat eaters?

A CASE FOR CHANGE

More than thirty years ago, Dr. T. Colin Campbell and his team at Cornell University, in partnership with researchers at Oxford University and the Chinese Government, embarked upon one of the most comprehensive studies of nutrition and health ever conducted: The China Project. This landmark study, combined with laboratory findings, looked at 65 counties, using extensive questionnaires and blood tests to gather information on 6,500 adults. When the researchers were done, they had more than 8,000 statistically significant associations between lifestyle, diet, and disease. The China Project was unmatched in terms of comprehensiveness, quality, and uniqueness, and conclusively demonstrated the dangers of a diet high in animal protein and the amazing health benefits of a whole food, plant-based diet. The study clearly concluded that the lower the percentage of animal protein consumed, the greater the health benefits. Even relatively small intakes of animal protein were associated with adverse effects. People who ate the most plant-based foods were the healthiest and tended to avoid chronic disease.

Indeed, animal fat from meat, chicken, egg, cheese and milk has been linked to a range of illnesses and conditions, including diabetes, rheumatoid arthritis, hypertension, heart disease, and various cancers.

Animal sources are likely to account for thirteen of the top fifteen sources of cholesterol-raising fats in the United States. The World Health Organization (WHO) has even classified processed meats like bacon and sausage as carcinogenic, in the same category as cigarettes!

The reality is that there are many vested interests at stake, which makes promoting plant-based nutrition a bit more difficult. The pharmaceutical industry and health insurance companies benefit financially from the model of treating disease symptoms. As sad and as corrupt as it may sound, sick people are big business. This isn't the fault of individuals per se, but an inevitable consequence of the fact that corporations have only one obligation, which is to improve their bottom line. And because a radical shift toward preventative medicine would annihilate their business model, many will do whatever they can to keep things the way they are.

Despite the existence of profit-centered industries, doctors, on the other hand, play a big role in balancing them out because they prioritize patient health in order to honor their sole purpose of helping people. As they now see the benefits and potential of plant-based nutrition, many doctors and nutritionists are advocating a plant-based diet and paving their own path, one that is separate from the rigid dogma of the current medical system. I love reading about how Dr. T. Colin Campbell, Dr. Joel Fuhrman, Dr. Michael Greger, Dr. John MacDougall, Dr. Dean Ornish, and Dr. Neal Barnard, to name a few, all strongly advocate for how we need to switch from a pharmaceutical-centered health care system to a nutrition-centered health care system. But they cannot continue to do this alone. We, as consumers and health advocates, need to be open to the idea of change and take matters into our own hands.

To make matters worse, demand has been shooting up as we ask for cheese-stuffed crusts, bacon bits on our breakfast waffles, and popcorn chicken as a movie snack. As a result, animal agriculture has become a massive industry. And just like we now mass-produce cars and T-shirts, eating animal products has become so commoditized that animal agriculture is as commercial, fast, cruel, and reckless as ever.

Factory farms need to produce cheap end products, and they need to produce them at extraordinary rates. So they keep up with this by treating farm animals the same way we treat equipment or machinery in a factory. Tens of billions of land animals per year are born into the factory-farm system and raised in deplorable conditions. They are fed unnatural diets full of antibiotics and have no room to move about freely. And while that might be good for business and the few people at the top who stand to profit greatly, factory farming is bad for everything else. It is cruel to the animals, destructive to the environment, and detrimental to human health. Think about this. The conditions in factory farms and slaughterhouses are so infection-inducing that the pharmaceutical industry sells 80 percent of all antibiotics made in the United States to animal agriculture—antibiotics that move through the bodies of animals and leave residues in their muscles and their milk. No wonder we are seeing people struggling with a higher risk of antibiotic resistance when they actually do get sick, which the WHO recently called "an increasingly serious threat to global public health." Not to mention the industrial, cancer-linked chemicals and toxins from these polluted conditions that we are keeping them in.

When you think about eating hormone-free or "cleaner" meat, here is something to think about: even if I take a well-raised cow, pamper her with a massage and a manicure and let her happily roam on grassy fields in very sanitary living conditions, she simply does not want to die. So as we push her into a slaughterhouse and she hears screams and sees the massacre around her, the reality is that she will be distressed, and those stress hormones are released into her body. Whether the cow was fed "organic" food or not, would we really want to be eating something carrying all that trauma?

Forget everything you know for a second. Forget the marketing or what grandma says or even that diet article you saved to help you lose that extra holiday weight. Let's ground ourselves with a fresh start. In the next few pages, I am going to share some thoughts with you. If you can take them in with an open mind, you can choose what to do with them, and you can make fresh, unbiased decisions accordingly. Most importantly, don't forget to do your own research as well! At the at the end of this book you will find references for all scientific data and journals quoted here as well as a list of documentaries and talks that I have enjoyed learning from.

THE PROTEIN PUZZLE

"But where do I get my protein from?"

One of the biggest misconceptions fueled by the fitness industry is that the only way to build muscles is to wolf down chicken breasts. This is largely misplaced. The reality is that a varied plant-based diet of whole grains, vegetables, and beans can easily meet your daily protein needs without the risks or the moral dilemma of having to consume animal products. There is no reason to believe that cutting animal products from your diet would equal protein deficiency.

A large research project conducted on plant-based diets was a cross-sectional study of 71,751 subjects, the Adventist Health Study 2 (AHS-2), which aimed to compare nutrient intakes between dietary patterns characterized by the consumption or exclusion of meat and dairy products. This study showed almost no discrepancy between vegan, vegetarian, and non-vegetarian protein intake, as sufficient intake from plants was resulting in a strikingly similar overall total protein intake.

Average Protein Intakes by Dietary Pattern

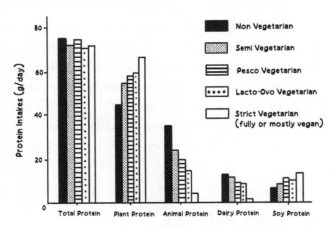

Just like the world's most muscular and strongest animals—the gorilla, the elephant, the rhino, and the giraffe—we can get our protein from plants! That's where the cows and chickens get it from too. So let's cut out the middlemen and get clean protein from plants; it comes without artery-clogging risks and fat streaks in our hearts, it's free of hormones and antibiotics, and it's simply better for our compassionate souls that thrive when we are protecting our fellow earthlings and the planet too.

Besides, have you really ever personally met someone with a protein deficiency?

In fact, most people on a standard American diet consume about double the amount they actually need. The current recommended dietary allowance for protein is 0.8 g protein/kg body weight/day for adults, which means that if you are, say, 70 kg (154 lb), you need to consume 60 grams of protein per day. But somehow, with the mass marketing of protein shakes and protein bars and with "chicken breast" on the poster of every new gym meal plan, we are getting much more, and when it comes to protein, more isn't always better. Studies have identified the adverse effects associated with long-term high animal protein intake in humans, which include increased cancer risk, disorders of liver function, disorders of bone and calcium homeostasis, disorders of renal functions and kidney stone development, and the progression of coronary artery disease, as foods rich in animal protein are also often packed with saturated fat and cholesterol.

THE CALCIUM CONUNDRUM

"But we need milk for calcium!"

Every single one of us was taught that we need to drink cow milk to get strong bones. What really startled me was watching a talk by James Wildman (do check it and other speeches out in the bibliography section of this book) where he said, "Cow milk. Why not dog milk?" If you really think about it, why not dog milk? Not chimpanzee milk, not elephant milk, not rhino milk, not giraffe milk, not cat milk, not hippo milk, not lion milk . . . somehow, we just need cow milk to get strong bones? The absurdity of drinking the milk from any other species and any other being besides our own mother, when it's said enough times, loses its absurdness. And that's how we live—in a story that we keep telling ourselves over and over so much so that we no longer question it.

There is no species in nature that just drinks the milk of another animal, claiming that they "need it," and there is no animal in nature that continues to drink milk after infancy. All mammals use their mother's milk to grow, but then they are instinctively weaned off of it when they no longer need it. Cows are not nature's milkshake machines; they just make milk after giving birth to turn their baby calves into big cows. Do you think something meant to turn a 200 kg baby calf to a 900 kg adult cow should be put into a 15 kg human toddler? Can you imagine the composition of that milk?

Composition of Milk from Different Species

Animal	Protein total %	Casein %	Whey protein %	Fat %	Carbohydrate %	Ash %
	1,2	0,5	0,7	3,8	7,0	0,2
	2,2	1,3	0,9	1,7	6,2	0,5
	3,5	2,8	0,7	3,7	4,8	0,7
	3,6	2,7	0,9	4,1	4,7	0,8
	5,8	4,9	0,9	7,9	4,5	0,8

Besides, approximately 65 percent of the human population is lactose intolerant, meaning they have a reduced ability to digest lactose after infancy. So chances are that you are too! I was invited over to my aunt's house for lunch once, and about half an hour before we sat down to eat, she took a small white pill. I wasn't planning on asking what it was, but she turned to me in excitement, wanting to reveal her big "life hack," and she said, "I discovered these pills that help me finally digest dairy without stomach cramps, so I take them before my meals." What? So if I get this correctly, our body refuses something and gives us natural signals like bloating and stomach cramps to beg us to stop eating it, but instead of just leaving the shredded cheese out of the pasta, we take medicine to help force it down and repress these symptoms. That seems rather extreme for a slice of cheesecake, don't you think?

Cultural stories, public policy on nutrition in many countries, and advertisements for dairy products link the increased consumption of calcium from milk to better bone health and the prevention of osteoporosis in later life. It's not a news flash that calcium is key for healthy bones. Getting enough calcium from childhood through adulthood helps build bones up and then helps slow the loss of bone as we age. It's not clear, though, if dairy products are really the best source of calcium, and they are definitely not the only source. One study has actually shown that populations that consume the highest quantities of cow milk and other dairy products have among the highest rates of osteoporosis and hip fracture in later life. It was consistently found that, when populations of people who eat different diets were compared, rates of hip fractures increased with increasing animal protein consumption, including increased dairy products. While that is not to say that milk consumption equals osteoporosis—as it is important to remember that scientifically, correlation does not directly prove causation—the overwhelming picture drawn by the data, in my view, is becoming harder to ignore.

Fractures/100,000 person-years

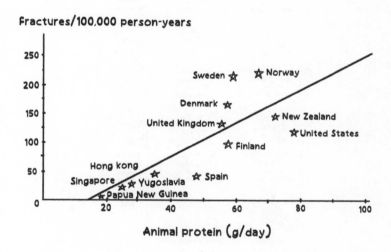

Animal protein (g/day)

But why have we been told to drink milk for "strong bones"? Because an entire industry thrives on making sure we do that. Marketing campaigns like "Got Milk?" were designed by corporations like the California Milk Processor Board, which were looking for creative strategies to boost sales. Marketing executives sat around a boardroom table and brainstormed ideas for increasing milk consumption to meet profit targets. At the end of the day, it is an industry that needs to sell a product.

Good sources of plant-based calcium are all around. Calcium-rich foods include seeds and green and leafy vegetables such as broccoli, cabbage, and okra, to name a few. But if you are really still worried about calcium, you can easily find fortified foods such as plant-based milks, cereals, and juices. Got almonds?

Why are we so obsessed with the idea of getting calcium from milk?

Cow milk, brand*
1 glass (240ml)
161 kcal
250 mg calcium

Soy milk, brand*
1 cup (224ml)
105 kcal
300 mg calcium

Chia seeds
3 tbsp (39g)
180 kcal
240 mg calcium

Tofu
½ cup (100g)
94 kcal
176 mg calcium

Chickpeas
1 cup (200g)
269 kcal
80.4 mg calcium

Orange juice, brand*
1 glass (240ml)
110 kcal
350 mg calcium

Almonds
½ cup (60g)
340 kcal
160 mg calcium

Soybeans
1 cup (172g)
296 kcal
175 mg calcium

Tahini
2 tbsp (32g)
210 kcal
50 mg calcium

Spinach, cooked
2 cups (360g)
97 kcal
410 mg calcium

Dried Figs
6 pieces (68g)
200 kcal
100 mg calcium

Tempeh
1 cup (166g)
320 kcal
184 mg calcium

Lentils
1 cup (198g)
230 kcal
37.6 mg calcium

Bok Choy
2 cups (140g)
18 kcal
147 mg calcium

Dried Apricots
10 pieces (80g)
200 kcal
80 mg calcium

White Beans
1 cup (260g)
220 kcal
120 mg calcium

Olives
1 cup (135g)
157 kcal
120 mg calcium

Farro
1 cup (150g)
200 kcal
176 mg calcium

Peas, edible-podded
2 cups (320g)
134 kcal
134 mg calcium

Green Beans
2 cups (240g)
80 kcal
106 mg calcium

Blackberries
1 cup (140g)
90 kcal
41 mg calcium

*store bought, fortified
All legumes and grains mentioned above are per cooked/boiled serving

PLANT LOVERS BY NATURE

"But we were born to eat meat."

We are not really born eating meat, because if you give a baby a grape and a rabbit, he will put the grape in his mouth, but he will not naturally try to eat the rabbit. We are *taught* to eat meat. And yes, humans *can* digest animal products, but just because we can eat something and possibly digest it, it doesn't mean we should. There are a lot of things that we *can* do as humans. We can smoke cigarettes, but we know they are terrible for us. We have access to drugs, but that doesn't mean we should hand them out at teenage parties. Because we have a fist to punch, should we punch our neighbors? The reality is that it is unnecessary to harm animals when there are alternatives. We *can* also live a long and healthier life without eating any animal products whatsoever.

Let's go back to our biological structure now. Who are we more like? A lion or a gorilla? We are actually most like our herbivore friends with very long intestines, carbohydrate digestive enzymes in our mouth, short and blunted teeth (with apple crunching "canines"), and jaws that open sideways for chewing vegetables, not up and down for biting into flesh.

	Carnivores	Omnivores	Herbivores	Humans
Facial Muscles	Reduced to allow wide mouth gape	Reduced	Well-developed	Well-developed
Jaw Type	Angle not expanded	Angle not expanded	Expanded angle	Expanded angle
Jaw Joint Location	On same plane as molar teeth	On same plane as molar teeth	Above the plane of the molars	Above the plane of the molars
Jaw Motion	Shearing; minimal side to side motion	Shearing; minimal side to side motion	No shear; good side to side, front to back	No shear; good side to side, front to back
Major Jaw Muscles	Temporalis	Temporalis	Masseter and pterygoids	Masseter and pterygoids
Mouth Opening vs. Head Size	Large	Large	Small	Small
Teeth: Incisors	Short and pointed	Short and pointed	Broad, flattened, and spade shape	Broad, flattened, and spade shape
Teeth: Canines	Long, sharp, and curved	Long, sharp, and curved	Dull and short or long (for defense), or none	Short and blunt
Teeth: Molars	Sharp, jagged, and blade shaped	Sharp blades and/or flattened	Flattened with cusps vs. complex surface	Flattened with nodular cusps
Chewing	None; swallows food as a whole	Swallows food as a whole and/or simple crushing	Extensive chewing necessary	Extensive chewing necessary
Saliva	No digestive enzymes	No digestive enzymes	Carbohydrate digesting enzymes	Carbohydrate digesting enzymes
Stomach Type	Simple	Simple	Simple or multiple chambers	Simple
Stomach Acidity with Food in Stomach	< pH 1	< pH 1	pH 4–5	pH 4–5
Length of Small Intestine	3–6 times body length	4–6 times body length	10–12+ times body length	10–11 times body length
Colon	Simple, short, and smooth	Simple, short, and smooth	Long, complex; may be sacculated	Long, sacculated
Liver	Can detoxify vitamin A	Can detoxify vitamin A	Cannot detoxify vitamin A	Cannot detoxify vitamin A
Kidney	Extremely concentrated urine	Extremely concentrated urine	Moderately concentrated urine	Moderately concentrated urine
Nails	Sharp claws	Sharp claws	Flattened nails or blunt hooves	Flattened nails

"But it's the way of the animal kingdom."

Yes, while animals do eat other animals all the time in nature, we don't need to base our own ethics as humans on the actions of animals. Nature also doesn't care about right or wrong, or whether something is fair, ethical or cruel. If we can justify something because animals do it, should we be killing babies like wild lions do, vomiting on people's food like flies, or urinating on other people's lawns like dogs? We can't justify a human behavior with one thing that animals do, which is eating animals, and not the rest. Besides, if humans had natural omnivorous instincts, we would be drooling and salivating over roadkill if we saw a squirrel crushed by a car. Instead, we can't even get ourselves to watch slaughterhouse footage, because seeing a dead animal shakes us to our core. Why? Because we care. We empathize. We understand that if these animals have eyes to see, ears to hear and a brain to think, then they also feel pain. They grieve over loss. They want to live.

THE "V" WORD

Let's talk about the "V" word. You may have heard the word "vegan" come up a lot. It's not a fad, it's not a buzzword, and it's not a diet. Veganism is the ethical belief that we do not need to harm animals to live.

This chapter started with the idea of changing our eating habits for health purposes with a whole food, plant-based diet. But there are also moral, logical, and ethical elements that come into play for most people. Let's look at the different definitions:

PLANT-BASED DIET: A diet consisting mostly or entirely of foods derived from plants, including vegetables, grains, nuts, seeds, legumes, and fruits. The emphasis here is on diet. Plant-based choices are often food choices for health purposes.

VEGAN: A person who does not eat or use animal products. The vegan society defines veganism as "a way of living which seeks to exclude, as far as is possible and practicable, all forms of exploitation of, and cruelty to, animals for food, clothing or any other purpose." Vegans go beyond their dinner plate, which happens to be plant-based as well, and avoid other forms of animal exploitation by not choosing products like leather when shopping for clothes or bags, not supporting animal captivity in zoos, and not buying cosmetics and beauty products that have been tested on animals.

I personally identify as vegan, and I encourage everyone around me to question how we treat animals today. I believe that peace begins on our plate, and to really be the best version of yourself is to invite peaceful energy, love, and compassion. We simply cannot live better just by choosing to eat better, but by being a force of kindness in society, standing up to unnecessary injustice, and sparking positive change in the world around us.

However, if you are not ready to call yourself "vegan," you do not need to put a label on your choices just yet. You will hear the word a lot throughout the book, but at first, focus on this transition. Focus on eating well and on causing less harm, focus on being at peace with your mind and with the world around you, and then, perhaps as early as the end of this book, or as late as a few years into your journey, you can decide what you would call it.

WHERE DO I GO FROM HERE?

You have made it this far because you are serious about making this change. You now see that we can not only survive but also thrive on a fully plant-based diet. Whether it was my personal story in Chapter 1 that kept you reading, or you were inspired by watching a friend, a family member, or a colleague transform their lives, or you too believe that this is the healthiest way to live, you are here because you are ready to embark on this journey. So where do you even start? Will this be a gradual change, or are you going to put this book down and run to the freezer and start throwing out leftover sausages from last spring's barbecue? Whatever you choose to do, I will be here to support you through this journey because I sure am grateful for everyone who was there during mine.

Together, we will break the process down into a few steps:

– **THE FIRST CLEANSE:** The body can hold on to toxins, so one optional way to start this journey is by planning your first juice detox with sample recipes and tips. We will also discuss other toxic energy sources in your surroundings to look out for.

- **TRANSITIONING YOUR FOOD:** This includes guides to:
  - Stocking up your pantry, shopping, and reading labels.
  - Replacing meat, eggs, and dairy in your favorite foods.
  - Easy-to-follow recipes and food combination ideas.
  - Eating out and ordering at restaurants.
- **FAMILY AND SOCIETY:** Talking about your new way of life with loved ones, raising kids, and finding a community.
- **MYTH BUSTING:** Helpful answers to some of the remarks you might hear at the dinner table.
- **SPIRITUAL IMPACT:** Transformations to anticipate beyond the physical benefits.

CHAPTER 3

THE BIG CLEANSE

Detox to kick-start your journey

Our food should be our medicine, and our medicine should be our food. But to eat when you are sick is to feed sickness.

—HIPPOCRATES, THE "FATHER OF MEDICINE"

Feeling unwell was my cue to start making major changes in my life; I had a feeling of heaviness, I was constantly tired, bloated, depressed, anxious, lethargic, and so on. But you don't have to wait for physical or medical symptoms to start changing your life. Waiting till your body presents these signs would often mean that it's already carrying the burden of leftover toxins.

If you do feel like your body might need a reboot, starting with a cleanse could be the best way to jump-start your new, healthier, plant-based journey. It helps you to put an end to addictive cravings for low nutritional value junk food, sugar, caffeine, nicotine, and soda, all of which I like to think of as addictive drugs in disguise. When our body is craving foods that are not good for it, it is time to pause and think about what we have programmed it to get used to and to desire. The body should be craving foods that help it grow and heal instead.

In this chapter, we will explore the fundamentals of a detox as an optional first step before you shift your overall food habits. The idea of a cleanse—and we will discuss how it will be both a physical and mental one—is to start a new chapter of your life without the heavy impact of your previous choices. This could help you restart and refresh your taste palates to start liking, and even craving, greens, supercharging your body with nutrients, and readjusting your energy as you prepare for your new, plant-based diet.

If you feel like you want to skip this chapter and jump directly into cleaner eating, that's okay too. You will find that in the next chapter.

WHY FASTING?

I fast for greater physical and mental efficiency.

—PLATO

Our bodies are naturally built to detox themselves. That's what the kidneys, liver, lungs, and skin do. However, as we have been putting so much strain on our bodies over time, years of junk food, chemical detergents, and stress sometimes overpower the process.

Fasting is probably the single greatest natural healing therapy. It is an ancient universal "remedy" that has been around for thousands of years, often talked about in literature by some of the greatest thinkers of past generations.

Fasting is the first principle of medicine, fast and see the strength of the spirit reveal itself.

—RUMI

If you think about it, almost every religion or spiritual practice has some form of fasting. Apart from physical well-being, it also has mental and spiritual benefits as it will push you to be more present, humble, and introspective, and will enable your spirit to be at ease.

When my cat Tom got sick, the first thing I noticed was that he stopped eating. I hadn't realized this before, but animals instinctively fast when they need to heal. And technically, so do we. When we have a cold, we lose our appetite and that's just our body's way of telling us to go easy on the digestion process to allow it to focus on its other functions to get better. This break gives our body the opportunity to go deeper into the healing process, because it is not busy with the process of digesting—instead, it can focus on rebuilding, rejuvenating, rebalancing, and eliminating the accumulated waste and toxins.

A little starvation can really do more for the average sick man than can the best medicines and the best doctors.

—MARK TWAIN

In 2010, Joe Cross, an Australian filmmaker, documented his journey on a sixty-day juice fast, which he embarked on after a lifetime of pizzas, burgers, and fries, in the movie, *Fat, Sick and Nearly Dead*. It ultimately helped him lose weight and combat his autoimmune disease without the help of medicines. He says the process reminded him of a scraped knee. Remember when you were a kid and fell off the monkey bars and got a bloody knee? Your parents kept telling you not to touch it. As long as you let it be, it would heal itself. If the body can heal itself on the outside, it can definitely do the same on the inside. We just need to give it a chance to do so.

Fasting cleanses and detoxing are especially recommended if you have symptoms such as:

BLOATING
FATIGUE
DIGESTIVE ISSUES   ALLERGIES
PUFFY EYES OR BAGS UNDER THE EYES
AUTOIMMUNE DISEASES
INFLAMMATION   LOW-GRADE INFECTION
IRRITATED SKIN
MENSTRUAL PROBLEMS

A JUICE FAST

One of the most common ways to allow your body to fast while still getting all your nutrients to empower it is a juice fast. A juice fast is simply a cleanse for a certain number of days (three to five days is a good start) where you eliminate all solid foods and only consume water and fresh, raw, cold-pressed juices. Such juices are usually packed with clean, plant-based ingredients that help boost your detoxification systems, flush out toxins, hydrate your cells, and nourish your body to jump-start your entire system and welcome a fresh start.

The fasting period not only gives your body a break from the process of digestion, but also helps you retrain your taste buds so you can stick to healthy, plant-based eating after the fast.

Blending versus juicing

The first thing to note, as you consider a juice fast, is that cold-pressed *juices* are very different from blended *smoothies*.

With smoothies, a blender pulverizes the ingredients and the pulp stays in; liquid is usually added to it, so the drink is usually thick and very filling. Smoothies can be integrated into everyday meal plans; they can act as a meal replacement and are still a great way to load up on nutrients!

But smoothies don't enable a cleanse.

For a cleanse, you would need juices instead. A juicer spins or squeezes your fruits and separates the pulp from the juice. Consuming juices without the pulp basically means removing the insoluble fiber out of the fruits and vegetables. You still get the soluble fiber and most of the vitamins and minerals inside the juice. This is what keeps your body in "fasting mode," because you are still getting nutrients, but giving your digestive system a break.

JUICER	BLENDER
Use to make juices	Use to make smoothies
Presses the ingredients Leaves only the soluble fiber and takes out the pulp (insoluble fiber) No additional liquid needed	Pulverizes the ingredients Both insoluble and soluble fiber remain inside Needs liquid added to it
A JUICE IS : • Not a meal replacement • Not as filling so more produce can be consumed • Great for cleanse/fast	A SMOOTHIE IS : • Meal replacement • Very filling • Not for a fast/cleanse

If you have a juicer at home

In this case, you can plan for the fast yourself. You can create your own juices and try to get around three liters of veggie-loaded juices per day.

If you don't own a juicer, that's okay too. Look for local juice cleanse programs in your neighborhood. Several companies can create the program and deliver the juices directly to you, freshly pressed, every morning.

If that isn't an option, you can also find certain bottled juices at your local supermarket, but you just need to take some care in choosing between brands and types of bottled juice.

Here are two things to look out for when buying bottled juice:

- Look for the term "cold pressed," "cold pasteurized," or "HPP" (high pressure processing) on the label. Unlike fresh juice, bottled juices are usually treated to kill pathogenic organisms to extend the shelf life of the product.
- Check the blend of bottled juices, particularly if you are cleansing. Many varieties can be heavy on fruit, and light on veggies. Look for about 80 percent vegetables and 20 percent fruit in your juice blends, whether fresh or bottled.

If you have a blender at home

Though a blender will not serve for a fast specifically, it would be great to make use of it to integrate green smoothies into your daily routine as an easy way to add more fresh produce to your diet. Most of us are not getting our daily recommended five to seven servings of vegetables and fruits. Green drinks (whether juices or smoothies) will help supercharge that. However, you have to mind the calorie count here, because we don't feel full as quickly when the food is in liquid form. So although this is a great way to integrate nutrients, smoothies can be heavy enough to be counted as meals.

Juice Recipes

If you choose to start your detox at home, here are some recipe examples to experiment with. You can follow your taste preferences, but a general good rule is to work up toward 80 percent of your juice coming from vegetables and 20 percent from fruits. If you don't think you are ready to gulp down that much spinach in your juice, don't let the 80 percent suggestion overwhelm you; just gradually build up to it. After all, over the course of the detox, you may find that your sweet tooth will subside, and you will develop a preference for juices with less natural sugars and more of a savory taste. Some people believe that they will never become accustomed to the stronger flavor of vegetable-based juices, but with time, our tastes change, and as your body starts to realize its true nutritional needs, it may even begin to prefer these juices that you once considered intolerable. I thought I would hate green juices at the start of my journey, but now I definitely pick them over the very sweet fruit-based ones.

Examples of Combinations to Shop For and Experiment With:		
Spinach	Beetroot	Celery
Kale	Carrot	Spinach
Apple	Apple	Cucumber
Pineapple	Pear	Apple
Cucumber	Kale	Pineapple
Melon		Ginger

My Personal Favorite Recipes

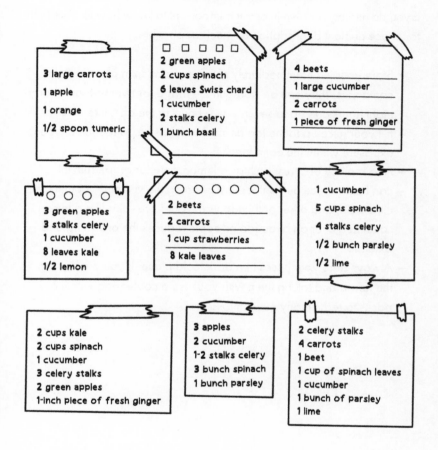

3 large carrots
1 apple
1 orange
1/2 spoon tumeric

2 green apples
2 cups spinach
6 leaves Swiss chard
1 cucumber
2 stalks celery
1 bunch basil

4 beets
1 large cucumber
2 carrots
1 piece of fresh ginger

3 green apples
3 stalks celery
1 cucumber
8 leaves kale
1/2 lemon

2 beets
2 carrots
1 cup strawberries
8 kale leaves

1 cucumber
5 cups spinach
4 stalks celery
1/2 bunch parsley
1/2 lime

2 cups kale
2 cups spinach
1 cucumber
3 celery stalks
2 green apples
1-inch piece of fresh ginger

3 apples
2 cucumber
1-2 stalks celery
3 bunch spinach
1 bunch parsley

2 celery stalks
4 carrots
1 beet
1 cup of spinach leaves
1 cucumber
1 bunch of parsley
1 lime

Storing your juices

If you do make your own juices, it is important to know how to store them to reduce nutrient degradation as much as possible:

- Store your juices immediately after preparation in glass airtight containers. They can be stored in the fridge for twenty-four to forty-eight hours and up to seventy-two hours at the absolute most.
- Fill your juice up to the top as much as possible to reduce oxygen exposure within the container.
- Add a piece of citrus, such as a lemon, lime, or grapefruit; this can help reduce nutrient loss by boosting the vitamin C content, citric acid, and other antioxidants in your juice—just like a lemon squeezed over an avocado or apple reduces the browning and oxidation.
- Always store your juices in a dark, cold place. If you are leaving the house and taking them with you, use a cooler bag with ice packs to reduce any nutrient loss.

DETOX DAYS

So you are ready with your juices and are about to start your first detox! Here are some steps to follow and some things to expect:

Pre-cleanse

First, lighten up your toxin load. Eliminate alcohol, coffee, processed meats, cigarettes, refined sugars, and saturated fats, all of which act as toxins in the body and are obstacles to your healing process.

Here are a few things you need to eliminate in your diet forty-eight hours prior to your cleanse, and by the end of this book, you could hopefully eliminate them for good:

- Animal products (meat, poultry, fish etc.)
- Dairy products
- Refined sugar
- Processed foods
- Nicotine
- Caffeine
- Alcohol
- Eggs

Incorporate more vegetables and fruits into your diet to get you prepared for your fast. Salads, sliced fresh fruits, and nuts are great examples. Remember to stay hydrated with room temperature water. You may slice up some cucumbers, limes, and mint leaves to make it easier to drink a large amount of water.

During the cleanse

Plan for at least six 500 ml/16 oz freshly-made juices every day, to be consumed within two-hour increments throughout the day.

Don't forget to hydrate well during the day. Water, water, water in-between your juices! This is crucial to your cleanse. If your detox reactions are getting intense, it's a sign that you should increase your water intake. Warm or room temperature water with a slice of lemon does wonders! Avoid drinking cold/iced water during cleansing to avoid troubling your digestive system. You can also include herbal tea during the day, but make sure it's caffeine free.

How water helps you fast

Keeps the body hydrated
Suppresses the appetite
Improves digestion
Helps prevent water retention and bloating
Helps flush toxins from the body
Stops the hunger versus thirst confusion

Working out will be great physically and mentally, but don't push yourself too hard. Your body needs to recover. Take the time to indulge in some yoga or mat Pilates, take a walk outside and immerse yourself in nature, jog lightly by the beach and float in the sea, or write about your thoughts, feelings, and the events that occurred inside a journal. This is a gracious time for you and your mental being to reconnect.

Your days may look something like this:

Day 1

MORNING: Energized, excited to start this process. First day of the rest of my life!

NOON: I'm really starting to get hungry. But it's okay, it's just my clock telling me it's lunch time. The reality is that I've got this!

AFTERNOON: Okay, I'm really starving now; there is no way I can do this for three days!

NIGHT: WHY AM I DOING THIS? Remind me again? I'm just going to sleep early to forget the emptiness in my stomach.

Day 2

MORNING: I have a terrible headache. I neeeeed caffeine.

NOON: Everyone is talking about lunch, and I can smell fresh bread everywhere. When I'm done with this, I'm going to eat six large pizzas.

AFTERNOON: I'm feeling kind of light-headed. A nap would be great right now.

NIGHT: This feels like torture, but weirdly enough, I'm getting kind of used to it.

Day 3

MORNING: I think these are caffeine withdrawal symptoms. I didn't realize I'm so addicted to coffee. Well, if I made it this far, maybe I'm not going to go back.

NOON: I miss chewing. But I feel kind of okay. I might just eat a banana after this fast. That's all I really want. Raw fruits.

AFTERNOON: Ugh . . . my colleague has the most ridiculous work problem. Life is about so much more than that.

NIGHT: I'm going to bed now, and I get to eat when I wake up. Wow, I don't even feel that hungry anymore. Actually, I don't mind sticking to this for a few more days!

The real impact of the detox happens between days 2 and 3. And after day 3 is when you start reaping the benefits. So if you can do this up to five days, you really should go for it!

Things to keep in mind

- **A DETOX IS NOT A WEIGHT-LOSS SOLUTION** and shouldn't be. In fact, though you may drop some weight on the scale, a lot of it would be water weight, which you will likely gain back.
- **YOU MAY FEEL TIRED OR GET A HEADACHE.** This could be due to many things, including caffeine withdrawal or dehydration. Drink a lot of water, and go easy on yourself. This is a cleansing process after years of accumulating toxins; it might get uncomfortable, but it's worth it.
- **IF YOU HAVE AN EATING DISORDER** or have had one in the past, do not resort to fasting.
- **FASTING AND HEAVY EXERCISING** at the same time may lead to low blood sugar, which can cause dizziness, confusion, and lightheadedness.
- **SEEK MEDICAL ADVICE** if you want to undergo a juice fast for more than seven days. You may also choose to do it in a retreat/center setup with qualified instructors. Fasting by people taking diabetes medications can lead to hypoglycemia and can lead to serious health issues.
- **AFTER THE FAST,** you might have the tendency to binge-eat. Just remember the hard work and why you started doing this. Your body just got a clean slate, and this is a chance to ignore the cravings of those pre-fast days and develop new habits.

IT'S NOT JUST FOOD!

As you are going through this cleanse, remember that toxins aren't just found in polluted air or because of poor food and drink choices. To really feel that desired sense of relief and clarity, you must look at all parts of your life. Are you inviting toxins in via other products touching your body? Are you accepting toxic energy from your surroundings?

Here are some things to think about:

SHIFTING TO NATURAL PRODUCTS: Our skin is the largest organ of our entire body and should really be treated with utmost care. Skin has pores that give external factors direct access into our body. Just like when we sweat and our skin releases water, it also absorbs what we put on it. Some chemicals, like parabens, sulfates, and synthetic dyes, are in our everyday products, and we rarely stop to think about their impact on our bodies. Shifting to natural products means less likelihood of breakouts, allergies, and inflammation. The way I like to think about it is: "If it's good to ingest, then it's typically great to apply on the skin."

CHOOSING CRUELTY-FREE: Was the facewash you used this morning tested on rabbits? What about your moisturizer? That lipstick may look great, but do you want to be putting something on your body that has subjected other living beings to cruel, painful testing methods? Think of the type of energy that product carries. Roughly 500,000 rabbits, guinea pigs, hamsters, rats, and mice die each year due to cosmetic testing alone. According to Humane Society International, animal tests for cosmetics include skin and eye irritation tests, where chemicals are rubbed onto the shaved skin or dripped into the eyes of these animals. These tests cause immeasurable pain and can cause blindness, swollen eyes, organ damage, and internal bleeding. Be conscious of how your products were made and look out for cruelty-free labels.

SURROUNDING YOURSELF WITH PEOPLE WHO LIFT YOU UP: My best friend keeps reminding me that there are just two types of people in the world: those who give you energy and those who take it away. Have you ever noticed that sometimes you walk out of a coffee date with an old friend feeling excited, alive, and ready for the world? And, at other times, a dinner date leaves you feeling exhausted and heavy? There are people, places, and things that make you feel like you are building your energy stores, that rejuvenate you and help you be at your best. Likewise, there are also people and places that drain you. Think about it. Is anyone in your life weighing you down? Do you have friends or family members you often don't want to see but you feel you "have to"? Perhaps your heart sinks a bit when you receive a text message from them? Or you may leave the house excited to see them but come back home feeling like your energy was just zapped? Whether they are in your life every day or show up from time to time, it is very important to assess these relationships and decide which ones lift you up and which ones don't. Here are some types of energies in people I try to avoid interacting with for too long when I need an energy boost. As you read through this, think about the people who surround you and if any of these traits are wearing you down. Keep in mind that most often, it is not about whether or not the person is a good or bad person; it's about whether or not they are the right energy type for you:

- **Jealousy:** If you tend to minimize your accomplishments in front of someone because you feel guilty about sharing good news, then that relationship is not constructive. Avoid people who can't be genuinely happy for you. Real friends won't try to diminish your successful moments to feel better about themselves.
- **Self-destruction:** Self-destructive people have no interest in growing or changing. They simply find contentment in complaining about their lives over and over again. They want your attention and perhaps your pity, but they're not really interested in solving their problems or driving positive change as they are comfortable with their status quo.

- **Trivial gossip:** Everybody partakes in some form of gossip. Whether it's workplace chatter, the sharing of family news, or celebrity heartbreaks, it's inevitable for people to talk about other people, and that's okay. But it is when it becomes malicious that it raises a red flag. Some people tend to "bully" others when they gossip. Sometimes, you may crave a meaningful conversation, but all you get in return is malevolent gossip.
- **Uncalled-for criticism:** Nobody is perfect. But just because you have flaws that you're struggling to overcome, it doesn't mean that someone should point them out to you all the time. There is a difference between someone trying to offer you constructive advice, and someone constantly pointing out your weaknesses just to attack you. If you have someone who is quick to emphasize your flaws and frequently criticizes your behavior, you risk them wearing down your self-esteem.

People can be different, but what energy drainers have in common is that after every interaction with them, you feel emotional fatigue and stress. When you are on a cleanse, think about the people who inadvertently lower your vibration (through thoughts, words, and actions) and how you can let go of carrying their negativity around.

GETTING RID OF DRAINING HABITS: Reflect on your day and the little habits you have. Does anything you do or that you get exposed to also feel draining? For example, one time, I moved desks at the office, and my new seat was right next to a corridor with a giant TV screen that played the news all day. This was right after the 2016 US presidential elections, and at least ten times a day, I was reading headlines that sounded like the world was falling apart. What was happening in the political world at that time fell outside my circle of control, so I did not need to be constantly reminded of it. When I realized the impact of the media on my energy and how I was going home feeling more anxious every day, I petitioned that the TV screen be switched off. I also blocked push notifications from all the news apps on my phone. It was life-changing and a habit I still carry today. Flashing headlines of negative news are a weight to carry. If it is information that you want to be exposed to, you can actively seek it and look it up. If it is breaking news that is important enough to impact your job or your family, it will find its way to you.

AFTER THE CLEANSE

During the first twelve hours after your cleanse, slowly incorporate fresh food back into your diet. Start with raw fruits that are easy to digest and stick to fruits and vegetables only on the first day. This is a new world you are venturing into, and your body is clean and ready for it. Your palate is a clean slate now, and your taste buds will embrace new, raw flavors, so this is the best time to decide to stick to a plant-based diet. That "craving" you once had for a cheesy pepperoni pizza with a glass of soda is gone, so this is your chance to change your relationship with food and let go of all those dangerous addictions that have been dictating your choices. This is also the best time to reflect on the type of energy you invite into your everyday life and its impact, not only on your own well-being but on the world around you. It's a chance to reset your dietary habits, restore your damaged cells, and boost your mental clarity and positive energy.

The next few chapters offer an easy guide to transitioning to a fully plant-based diet, including what to eat and how to shop for products. They also contain ideas to replace animal products in your everyday, favorite dishes.

CHAPTER 4

SO . . . WHAT DO I EAT?

How to bring your food back to nature

Now that you are clear on your decision to stick to plant-based food, whether it is a decision you made for your health or because you learned about veganism which you now believe is a lifestyle that allows you to live more peacefully by inflicting less harm on other creatures and on the planet, the defining principles remain the same: to fuel your body with food that allows it to thrive, that is as close as can be to its natural form, and that causes as little harm as possible.

The actual definition of food is "any nutritious substance that people or animals eat or drink or that plants absorb in order to maintain life and growth." *Nutritious.* That's what food is. It is our fuel. Our body converts it into energy in order to function. Food enables our body to grow and repair itself, and the type of food we eat affects the efficiency of this process. Just like we fill up our cars with good quality gas, we can't fuel our bodies with junk and expect them to run.

So . . . what do I eat? Pretty much anything so as long as it doesn't come from an animal. Animal food products are essentially:

– Any type of meat or poultry (beef, chicken, turkey, pork etc.)
– Fish and shellfish
– Dairy products (cow milk, dairy cheese, butter, cream etc.)
– Eggs
– Honey
– Other animal-derived ingredients such as gelatin, casein, whey, carmine, shellac etc. Foods containing these ingredients include some types of marshmallows, whey-based protein bars and supplements, and gummy candies.

The idea of avoiding all the above animal products may sound overwhelming. A reaction I commonly get is, "But if you don't eat meat and cheese, then there is nothing you *can* eat!" But just think about the handful of meats I listed above that people eat (beef, chicken, fish, turkey etc.). Now consider all the variety of plant-based foods out there: lentils, beans, avocadoes, peas, pumpkins, tomatoes, zucchini, eggplants, potatoes, bananas, chickpeas, beetroots, freekeh, carrots, spinach, artichokes, mangoes, corn, peanut butter, walnuts, coconuts, most breads, chocolate (without added milk), plums, berries, oranges, oats . . . the list goes on! The point is, I can think of five to six "meats" but hundreds of fruits, vegetables, grains, and nuts. The combinations of tasty, healthy plant-based foods are endless, and your diet can be rich with variety and choices.

I know at first this transition may seem almost impossible, but don't worry, you can do this! I can assure you that many people start out feeling confused and worried, and in just a few weeks, they realize that there are plenty of delicious and nutritious foods and plant-based alternatives to all of their favorite meals. Then, this new lifestyle just becomes their natural new way of eating, and they love it. What is most important is to approach this new chapter in your life with an open mind and a positive attitude. Try to always remember all the things you are gaining from taking this step instead of what you are missing out on.

What I found works well with most people is to clearly articulate why you are embarking on this journey. That usually helps you to stay positive and motivated. When it comes to eating, your new diet shouldn't be about willpower, deprivation, or struggle because once you learn more about plant-based eating, you will realize there isn't much you have to "give up." Find the reasons that drive you and inspire you, and write them down somewhere that you glance at every day. I find writing little notes and sticking them on my desk, fridge, or bathroom mirror helpful. Here are some ideas to write down:

I choose a whole food, plant-based diet because
I love my body and choose to treat it with
care by fueling it with what is best for it.

Today, I will live in alignment with my values by
making sure no other sentient beings had to
suffer for whatever ended up on my plate.

I have seen people I love struggle with preventable
diseases, and I choose to do my best to
lower my risk of heart disease and type 2
diabetes by shifting my food choices.

I now believe that to truly live well means to
exist while causing as little harm as possible
to this planet and its resources.

Today, I choose to be the best version of myself,
and that means I will be healthy, kind to all creatures,
and conscious of my impact on the planet.

I choose to be a green citizen of this planet and reduce
my environmental impact for the generations to come.

I am a compassionate person; I will live on this planet
in peace, and I choose not to harm other earthlings.

There are plenty of good reasons to eat a plant-based diet and even more good reasons beyond your dinner plate to be vegan. Which one speaks to you? Keep that reason front and center to help you stay focused. This will be your morning affirmation and your reminder for why you are doing this. As with any big lifestyle change, it's going to get tough at times, so having a clear reason why can help you stick to your goals.

After being clear on what drives you, empower yourself with the knowledge of what and how to eat. While it is true that we have industrialized animal products so much that they are found in most common meals, I don't believe it's difficult to cut them out if you know just what to eat, how to read labels, and how to prepare quick meals. Once you're familiar with the ins and outs of vegan alternatives to your favorite foods and to everyday quick picks like pizza, cookies, chocolate, and sandwiches, you'll have no problem learning to love your new lifestyle and how it makes you feel.

SHOPPING AND STOCKING UP

You may be wondering where to start. Just take a look in your kitchen. You will notice that most items in your pantry are already vegan! Peanut butter, baked beans, many breakfast cereals, jam, dried pasta, rice, most breads, hash browns, coconut milk, lots of curry pastes, herbs, spices, ketchup and mustard, pickles, olive oil and vegetable oils, soy sauce, fruit juice, tea and coffee, lots of biscuits, crackers, chips, crispbreads, and, of course, fruits and vegetables—fresh, dried, canned, and frozen. Perhaps, for a real fresh start, you can go through your kitchen and donate whatever items you no longer choose to eat. Or if other members of your family are not embarking on this journey with you and they usually do the shopping, be clear to them about your food choices so they don't get those specific items in the future, or at least so they manage the quantities to minimize food wastage.

As you start deliberately preparing for your new lifestyle, start by planning your meals and writing down a shopping list. Whether you're a beginner or an experienced plant-based eater, a list will be helpful as you navigate the grocery store. Let's cover some basic foods that you might find helpful to have around the house or that might just give you ideas to create your own meal plan. Depending on your dietary preferences, each week, your grocery list might consist of some staple foods within the following 3 Ps:

- **PRODUCE:** A lot of fruits and vegetables, fresh and frozen.
- **PANTRY ITEMS:**
  · **Legumes.** Chickpeas, lentils, beans, peanuts.
  · **Whole grains.** Such as oats, brown rice, and quinoa, and whole grain products such as popcorn, bread, and pasta.
  · **Nuts and seeds.** Including nut butters and spreads but also raw almonds, walnuts, cashews, chia seeds, hemp seeds, pumpkin seeds, sesame seeds, and sunflower seeds.

- · **Herbs and spices.** Fresh like basil, coriander, and rosemary, and dried like cumin, thyme, and curry powder or paste, depending on your taste preferences.
- · **Natural sweeteners.** Agave syrup, molasses, and maple syrup.
- · **Soy products and dairy alternatives.** Fresh soy products such as tofu, tempeh, and edamame, and dairy alternatives like almond or cashew milk and dairy-free yogurt.
- **PACKAGED ITEMS:** Though it's best to limit processed foods, some convenient snacks are made consciously and with no preservatives; these include some cereals, spreads, or healthy crackers.

Remember that although, for you, this may purely be about avoiding animal products, ideally you should also be shopping for nutrients. The ultimate objective is filling your cart with enough nutrient-dense foods to cover your nutrient and calorie needs while minimizing processed foods that are high in sugar and sodium. Focus on loading up on vitamins and fibers with leafy greens and colorful fruits and vegetables, unrefined carbohydrates/starches such as potato, sweet potato, rice, oats, and quinoa, some sources of healthy fats such as avocado, olive oil, tahini, and seeds, and some sources of protein such as lentils, beans, nuts, tofu, tempeh, and edamame.

When you're not sure if they'll get that vegan product back in

PRODUCE

Fresh vegetables would make up the bulk of your diet. Mom was right, vegetables are an essential food group that are needed to cover all your micronutrient needs. They're rich in fiber, antioxidants, vitamins, and minerals. We need all of these things for a properly functioning body and to help prevent chronic disease and nutrient deficiencies. If you struggle with getting enough greens into your diet, remember the green juices and smoothies in the previous chapter and how they can help you sneak vegetables into your day. Juices and smoothies are also particularly useful if you end up buying too much produce, as they can help you prevent food waste while increasing your nutrient intake.

My vegetable shopping list varies based on my weekly meal plan. However, staples like lettuce, spinach, beets, broccoli, carrots, zucchini, eggplant, and sweet potato are always on my list. Though fresh is great, if buying some frozen vegetables will help you stick to healthy eating, go for it! I often stock up on emergency frozen green beans, spinach, artichokes, Brussels sprouts, and mixed stir-fry veggies.

Fruits are also excellent nutritious foods to enjoy daily. They are great as a snack or dessert and are a healthy breakfast option too. Bananas, apples, oranges, and berries are staples at my home. Just like vegetables, I always try to buy fresh fruit, but frozen fruits are also useful for smoothies and baking. I also freeze leftover fruits that are getting too ripe to make sure I get a chance to eat them later, especially bananas! Frozen bananas are the perfect base for homemade ice cream, açaí bowls, and frozen fruit bowls. You will find some ideas and recipes for these in the next two chapters.

Though fresh and frozen fruits are best, within limits, dried fruits are also great on the go or as trail mixes with nuts or with breakfast cereals.

Here are some produce shopping list ideas to look out for:

IN THE VEGETABLE SECTION	IN THE FRUIT SECTION	IN THE FREEZER SECTION	SNACKS/ REFILLABLE AISLES
Leafy greens: Kale, spinach, arugula, collard greens	Banana	Berries: blueberries, raspberries, strawberries, mixed berry blends	
Cruciferous veggies: cauliflower, broccoli, cabbage, Brussels sprouts	Apple		
	Pear		
	Kiwi		
	Dates		
Root vegetables: parsnips, carrots, sweet potato, yams, potatoes, turnips, rutabagas	Watermelon	Cherries	
	Cantaloupe	Mango	
	Honeydew	Mixed fruits	
	Pomegranate	Pineapple	
	Figs	Peach	
	Apricots		
Zucchini	Nectarines		
Cucumber	Plums	Spinach	
Tomato	Peaches	Artichokes	
Asparagus	Cherries	Green beans	Cherries
Beets	Grapes	Brussels sprouts	Apricots
Bell peppers	Avocado		Figs
Carrots			Mango
Artichokes			Raisins
Tomatoes of all varieties	Berries: blueberries, strawberries, raspberries		Cranberries
			Dates
Hot peppers			Mulberries
Celery	Citrus fruits: lemons, limes, oranges, grapefruits, clementine, apricot		Goji berries
Onions			Banana chips
Shallots			Sun-dried tomatoes
Mushrooms			
Garlic			
Eggplant	Tropical fruits: papaya, mango, dragon fruit, lychee, pineapple, passionfruit, durian, guava, jackfruit		
Ginger			
Sweet potatoes and yams			
Potatoes			
Squash: butternut, acorn, kabocha, pumpkin			
Zucchini			
Legumes: green beans, green peas, snap peas, snow peas			
Corn			
Peas			
Pumpkin			
Artichokes			

Local and Seasonal

When buying fruits and vegetables, try to also choose locally grown or locally produced food that is in season.

Why locally grown?

Eating local produce usually means choosing fruits and vegetables that have been grown close to home. This is not only good for the local economy and the environment—local food doesn't have to travel as far to arrive on your plate, which helps reduce greenhouse gas emissions and contributes to improving your carbon footprint—but it also often ends up being more nutritious. Produce such as broccoli, green beans, kale, red peppers, tomatoes, apricots, and peaches are susceptible to nutrient loss when harvested and transported from longer distances, while produce that is heartier, such as apples, oranges, grapefruit, and carrots, keeps its nutrients even if it travels to get to you.

Why seasonal?

Besides tasting better, foods that are grown and consumed during their appropriate seasons are usually more nutritionally dense. When foods are grown out of season, they are unable to follow their natural growing and ripening rhythms. In order for certain fruits and vegetables to be available year-round, post-harvest treatments, known as ripening agents, are used. These include chemicals, gases, and heat processes. Some produce is also coated with an edible film to protect it. These processes allow foods to be produced in mass quantities by slowing the maturation and ripening process. They also help to protect the produce from bacteria and other pathogens on its long journey from the fields to your local grocery store. So while this process ensures that farmers can meet consumer demand year-round, and we are grateful for that when we really need blueberry pancakes in January, researchers have found that artificially ripened produce is often not as nutritious or tasty as naturally ripened produce.

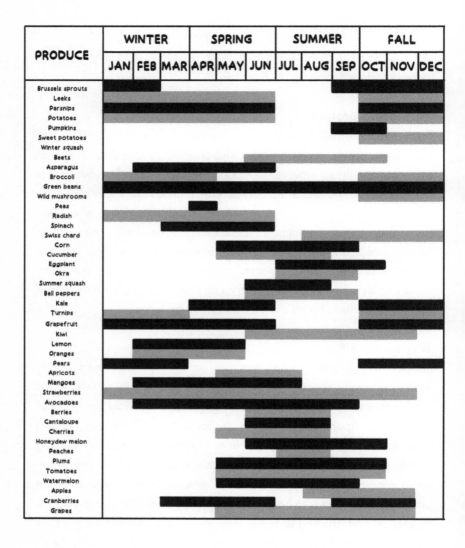

PANTRY

Legumes

Legumes include beans, chickpeas, lentils, and peanuts. This is probably my favorite grocery category, as legumes make up a big part of my diet. Legumes are a great source of protein in a plant-based diet, and they provide many essential vitamins, minerals, and antioxidants, besides being rich in fiber. I often buy dried beans and lentils in bulk and keep them at home to cook throughout the month. Dried beans and chickpeas need to be soaked overnight so they can cook quickly and become easier to digest, but lentils cook faster and don't require soaking if you are in a hurry. If you need to use jar/canned legumes in your transition phase for more convenience and easier cooking, go for it, and don't let having to presoak them stop you from getting your source of legumes every day!

Whole grains

From quinoa to freekeh and millet, there's more to grains than just bread. Often just labeled as "carbs," grains have gotten a bad reputation over the years, thanks to white bread which has been deemed as the all-evil enemy. Yes, the reality is that processed white bread—sold off the shelf with refined wheat, white sugar, powdered milk, and margarine—isn't great because the refined grain loses nutrients in the making, and all those extras are not really needed for anything more than taste and preservation.

Whole grains, though, have several nutritional benefits packed in all three parts of the seed or the kernel of the grain. The three parts of the seed include the bran, or the outermost layer of the grain, where most of the fiber is found, making whole grains excellent for digestion and gut health. The bran is also rich in B vitamins, such as niacin, thiamin, and folate, and contains important minerals such as zinc, iron, and magnesium as well as a small amount of protein. Next you'll find the endosperm, which is the biggest part of the grain, where you'll find carbohydrates, protein, and a small amount of vitamins and minerals. Finally, the smallest, innermost part is the germ, and it provides a large amount of B vitamins, vitamin E, and minerals. When grains are therefore refined and made into products such as white flour, some or all of the germ and bran are removed. This allows them to have a finer texture and improves their shelf life, but it also removes dietary fiber, iron, and many B vitamins, causing the grain to lose much of its nutritional value. So next time you are about to order a plate of pasta, remember the difference between "white" and whole wheat.

Whole Grain vs. "White" Grain

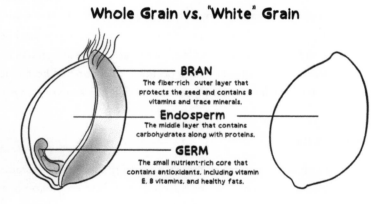

BRAN
The fiber-rich outer layer that protects the seed and contains B vitamins and trace minerals.

Endosperm
The middle layer that contains carbohydrates along with proteins.

GERM
The small nutrient-rich core that contains antioxidants, including vitamin E, B vitamins, and healthy fats.

Stock up on some everyday whole grains like quinoa, barley, brown rice, bulgur, oats, and farro, and you can buy the rest whenever you need them. As for flours, try gram flour or quinoa flour and use whole wheat flour occasionally, while baking.

Nuts and seeds

Nuts and seeds are also wonderful, nourishing foods that act as a source of good dietary fat and protein. They are rich in nutrients like vitamin E, iron, calcium, omega-3 fatty acids, zinc, and magnesium. Stock up on raw almonds, walnuts, cashews, chia seeds, hemp seeds, pumpkin seeds, sesame seeds, and sunflower seeds as everyday snacks or as toppings to your smoothies, oatmeal, and breakfast cereals. Don't forget nut butters as well. I love peanut butter, but almond butter is great too; just make sure the brand you pick has no added sugar.

Herbs and spices

Having a well-stocked pantry of dried herbs and spices will not only help you create fun, flavorful meals but is also quite beneficial. Both dried and fresh herbs and spices are rich in antioxidants and have many beneficial and anti-inflammatory properties. I personally add cumin and coriander to almost every stew I make, but as you start experimenting with your favorite flavors, you will get a better sense of what herbs and spices you always need in your pantry. For fresh herbs, especially basil, rosemary, and oregano, I highly recommend starting your own small herb garden at home. These plants are usually small, and you don't need a big outdoor garden for them, just a pot of soil and some sunlight. As you will be eating less processed food, your sodium intake will naturally be lower, so a good quality sea salt, in moderation, can also be a healthy addition to your diet.

Natural sweeteners

Whether or not you use sweeteners in your kitchen is up to you. You may find dates, bananas, agave syrup, molasses, and maple syrup great for smoothies and pancakes. For white sugar replacements during cooking, you can use coconut sugar or stevia.

Soy products and dairy replacements

We will discuss these in more detail in the next chapter, but as you begin your transition, it's important that you keep some of your favorite everyday meals by making small adjustments to them. Tofu scrambled eggs, oat milk hot chocolate, soymilk with cereal, and soy-based cooking cream with nutritional yeast for a cheesy creamy pasta are a few examples. Soy products are an excellent source of protein and other nutrients, and plant-based milks tend to be fortified with vitamins D, B12, and B2 (riboflavin).

Try and avoid highly processed dairy replacements. If you are starting out, you can consider items such as vegan cream cheese, vegan sour cream, chocolate soy or almond milk, dairy-free ice cream, or packaged vegan cheese slices. However, eventually it would be good to look out for healthier alternatives such as homemade cashew cheese, coconut yogurt, and dairy-free milks with no added sugars such as almond, oat, soy, rice, or coconut.

Dried foods/ refillable section (can buy in soaked jars/ cans if hard to cook)	Grains/ refillable section	Nuts and seeds	Herbs and spices	Condiments	Sweeteners and baking	Common meat and dairy replacements	Snacks and packaged foods
Chickpeas	Rice: brown rice, wild rice, black rice	Pecans Almonds Walnuts Hazelnuts Pistachios Peanuts (legume)	Dried: basil, bay leaves, cumin, cinnamon, chilli powder, red pepper flakes, cayenne pepper, paprika, curry powder (or paste), turmeric, thyme, oregano, rosemary, dill, black peppercorns, sea salt/pink Himalayan salt	Tomato paste Coconut milk (for cooking) Red/yellow curry paste Soy sauce or gluten-free tamari Sweet chili sauce Salsa Organic ketchup Egg-free mayo Miso paste Nutritional yeast	Agave syrup Maple syrup Molasses Applesauce Baking powder Baking soda Cornstarch Pure vanilla extract Shredded coconut Coconut flakes	Soy yogurt (unsweetened) Coconut yogurt Cashew cheese Dairy-free milk of choice (such as almond, oat, soy, rice, or coconut) Nutritional yeast	Peanut butter (or any nut butter: almond, cashew, hazelnut) Corn kernels (for popcorn)
Beans: white, kidney, fava black eyed, pinto Green beans Lentils: brown, red, yellow Peas Split peas	Bulgur Oats/oatmeal Quinoa Farro Freekeh Millets Amaranth Buckwheat Barley Whole wheat pasta	Chia seeds Flaxseed (whole not ground) Hemp seeds Sunflower seeds Pumpkin seeds Sesame seeds	Fresh herbs (when needed): basil, coriander (cilantro), parsley, chives, rosemary	Vinegar: apple cider, white, and balsamic Tahini	Various flours such as chickpea flour, quinoa flour, coconut flour, almond flour	Tofu of all varieties Tempeh Edamame Jackfruit (canned)	Pretzels Rice cakes Dark chocolate Cereals

PACKAGED FOOD AND SNACKS

This chapter has so far been about the foods that you need to fuel your body. The healthiest foods are those that come straight out of the garden and are consumed in their natural form or as simply prepared as possible. As you start feeling the benefits of this transition, you may want to eat a 100 percent whole food plant-based diet 100 percent of the time, and that would be amazing. Fresh fruits, vegetables, legumes, and intact whole grains should be at the core of a healthy lifestyle.

However, the long-term sustainability of this new lifestyle is the number-one priority, so there's also nothing wrong with including some lightly processed prepackaged foods in your diet every so often at first, if that helps you stick to it. I have learned from many people who have asked for my guidance during this period that changing your eating habits is a big undertaking, and these types of foods may be particularly helpful. Try not to get stressed about putting things into "good" and "bad" categories. After all, just the fact that you are eliminating processed animal products from your diet is already a significant leap toward healthier eating. Sure, food should be our powerful, nutrient-packed fuel, but sometimes it can be a source of comfort too.

Vegan meat and dairy alternatives may be especially helpful as you transition away from an animal-product-heavy diet. There are plenty of decent alternatives to dairy available today. There are also plenty of branded snacks and packaged foods that cater to this consumer need, as well as simply "accidentally" vegan products (like Oreos) out there.

Accidentally vegan

You will find that some store-bought items, especially packaged snacks, are accidentally vegan. A lot of spreads, biscuits, crisps, and chocolates simply don't contain animal products. Some off-the-shelf cakes and pancake mixes, for example, don't include dairy but ask you to add milk and eggs, which you can easily substitute with plant-based milk and mashed bananas.

It is great if you just wanted to go vegan to prevent animal cruelty. But remember that just because something is vegan, it does not automatically mean that it is healthy. As you look at the labels, it would be great if you look out for not just animal products but additives and ingredients and make decisions accordingly. You will find that, at the same time, there are some packaged and processed foods that can be included as part of a healthy diet and, in fact, keeping some of them around and on hand can make following a healthy diet easier.

Reading labels

One of my favorite experiences in hunting for plant-based foods was "having to" read labels. We really don't realize what is going into our bodies until we start noticing how many ingredients we consume that we can't even pronounce. It suddenly occurred to me that before going vegan, I had no idea what was in the food I ate. Now, since I "have to" make a deliberate effort to check and see if the products contain any animal derivatives anyways, I also look out for any unhealthy additives. Packaged and processed foods are usually loaded with fats, free oils, salt, refined sugars/sweeteners, and refined carbohydrates/grains. They are also almost always calorie dense. My general rule has become to pick out packaged food with as few ingredients as possible, and if I can't pronounce it, it's probably not food.

Check out the difference between these two bread labels I spotted at the grocery store. Which one would it make more sense to buy? It's bread at the end of the day. Homemade bread is usually made up of four ingredients: flour, yeast, water, and salt.

INGREDIENTS: UNBLEACHED ENRICHED FLOUR (WHEAT FLOUR, MALTED BARLEY FLOUR, NIACIN, REDUCE IRON, THIAMINE MONONITRATE, RIBOFLAVIN, FOLIC ACID, WATER, HIGHT FRUCTOSE CORN SYRUP, YEAST, CONTAINS 2% OR LESS OF EACH OF THE FOLLOWING: CALCIUM CARBONATE, SOYBEAN OIL, WHEAT GLUTEN, SALT, DOUGH CONDITIONERS (CONTAINS ONE OR MORE OF THE FOLLOWING: SODIUM STEAROYL LACTYLATE, CALCIUM STEAROYL LACTYLATE, MONOGLYCERIDES, MONOX AND DIGLYCERIDES, DISTILLED MONOGLYCERIDE, CALCIUM PEROXIDE, CALCIUM IODATE, DATEM, ETHOXYLATED MONO- AND DIGLYCERIDES, ENZYMES, ASCORBIC ACID), VINEGAR, MONOCALCIUM PHOSPHATE, YEAST EXTRACT, MODIFIED CORN STARCH, SUCROSE, SUGAR, SOY LECITHIN, CHOLECALCIFEROL (VITAMIN D3), SOY FLOUR, AMMONIUM SULPHATE, CALCIUM SULPHATE, CALCIUM PROPIONATE (TO RETARD SPOILAGE).

Ingredients:
Wheat Flour (flour, folate, thiamine),
Chia Seeds (3.3%),
Filtered Water, Iodized Salt.

Allergen:
contains Wheat and Gluten.

At first, it can sometimes be frustrating trying to figure out which foods contain hidden animal ingredients. But reading labels will eventually become super easy. Don't panic about the long list below of "things to look out for." It's a good guide that in no time at all will become intuitive, and you will become an *expert label "speed reader."*

Before skimming through all the ingredients, here are three shortcuts you can use:

— Check your local store's vegan section for a pre-vetted selection.
— Look for a "vegan" label on the product. Note that "dairy-free," "lactose-free," or "free from" labels don't necessarily mean that the product is vegan, so double-check the ingredients.
— Look at the allergen section at the bottom of the ingredients. Since milk is an allergen, the product might directly point out, "Contains Milk" so you wouldn't have to go through the whole ingredient list to know that.

Keep in mind that if a food product doesn't have milk in the ingredients but the label says "may contain traces of milk," it is still suitable for vegans.

It generally means that the food is produced in a shared facility where dairy products are also produced, so there may be cross contamination, and it is therefore indicated for allergy purposes.

Hidden things to look out for

Apart from meat, milk, and eggs, some animal by-products may not necessarily be obvious. Below are other ingredients to look out for:

- Whey, casein, and lactose—from milk
- Collagen, keratin, and elastin—usually from the skin, bones, and connective tissues of animals
- Gelatine/gelatin—from boiling animal skin, tendons, ligaments, and/or bones
- Aspic—industry alternative to gelatin made from meat stock
- Lard, tallow, and ghee—animal fats
- Shellac and carmine—obtained from insects
- Honey, propolis, and royal jelly—produced by bees
- Albumen/albumin—from eggs
- Cod liver oil—from fish, found in some lotions, vitamins, and supplements

In addition to this, food additives are often given an "E number," which can make navigating labels a bit more difficult. Many of these E numbers are not from animal sources; however, there are a few to look out for that are not cruelty-free. Some common ones include:

- E120: Carmine, also known as cochineal, carminic acid, or natural red 4. They are crushed up beetles used as red food coloring.
- E441: Gelatine. A gelling agent made from ground up animal bone and skin, often found in confectionery.
- E542: Bone phosphate. Ground up animal bones used to keep foods moist.

- E901: Beeswax. As the name suggests, this is wax that's made by bees and is used as a glazing agent.
- E904: Shellac. Glazing agent made from the secretions of an insect called the lac bug.
- E910, E920, E921: L-cysteine and its derivatives. Made from animal hair and feathers, these additives are found in some breads as a proving agent.
- E913: Lanolin. A waxy substance extracted from the wool of sheep and other woolly animals. Mostly used in cosmetics.
- E966: Lactitol. A sweetener derived from lactose, which is made from milk.

While that may seem like a long list, there are plenty of foods that are made without any of the above ingredients, and, once you know what to look out for, it becomes easy to spot nonvegan foods.

CHAPTER 5

COMMON REPLACEMENTS

Because old taste buds die hard

A new awareness of the variety of plant-based foods and ingredients could push you to start experimenting with new textures and flavors. However, as hard as you try to stick to simply eating whatever nature has to offer in its original raw form, you might still be craving foods you have gotten used to over the years: a warm slice of pizza, a Saturday afternoon barbecued burger, Mama's stroganoff, or soggy afternoon cereal in a bowl of cold milk. The great news is that you can pretty much get a vegan version of any of your favorite meals!

As you test out different whole food combinations, you will find similar textures to replace your main meat or dairy ingredients. Nutritional yeast has the same "cheesy" flavor of parmesan cheese, jackfruit has the same texture as shredded cooked chicken, and lentils make for a great mincemeat substitute in a bolognese recipe.

Meanwhile, in supermarkets, you will find convenient products that are so similar to the foods you love and that just don't contain animal products. You will find vegan chocolates, cake mixes, mayonnaise, dressings, and many more everyday items. Explore the fridges to find a range of plant-based milk (soy, oat, almond, coconut, hemp, rice, and more) and plant-based cheeses and yogurts in various flavors. In the freezer section, you will find burgers, sausages, and plant-based chicken, fish, and beef mince substitutes. And don't forget to check out the ice-cream section for coconut, almond, or soy-based tubs.

In this chapter, let's explore some common substitutes for dairy, eggs, and meat to help you experiment with new flavors but also keep some of your longtime favorites in your everyday meals.

DONE WITH DAIRY

I know, I know, "but cheeeeesssee." Most people I meet who are considering going vegan say, "I can easily ditch the meat, but ohhhh, cheese." I understand, in a way, because I love my homemade plant-based cheeses! They are healthier, easy to make, and more delicious; plus, they do the trick without the hormone- and antibiotic-infused baby calf growth fluid.

Plant-based cheeses are becoming more easily available. They are found in retail stores, have a relatively long shelf life, and are often made of cashews, soy or coconut oil. Though many brands out there are excellent, you may not directly find the perfect brand to suit your taste as it is a relatively new and fast-growing segment. So this is one area where you will have to experiment with different flavors, textures, and brands.

Other than ready-made cheeses, there is nutritional yeast. Nutritional yeast, also known as "nooch," has quickly become one of *the* go-to substitutes for cheese or a cheesy flavor. I know the name may not sound so appetizing, but I promise that the taste certainly is. This deactivated yeast product is usually yellow in color, which makes it look even more cheese-like in your dish, and it has a savory, nutty, and cheesy flavor.

Nutritional yeast comes either in the form of flakes or as a powder, so the easiest way to use it is by sprinkling it over dishes such as pasta, as an alternative to parmesan cheese flakes. It also makes a great popcorn or soup topping! Nutritional yeast is available to buy in some grocery stores and health food shops, as well as online.

Meanwhile, the plant-based milk options are hard to get wrong. Most of them taste great but, again, you would have to experiment to find your perfect cup of plant-based milk. Some of the most common varieties you would find include soy, almond, coconut, rice, oat, hemp, and hazelnut milk.

Though personal taste preferences play a big role, here are some other factors that could help you determine your milk of choice:

Which Milk Should I Choose?

1 Cup	Environmental impact of one cup			Nutritional values of one cup				
	EMISSIONS (kg)	LAND USE (sq m)	WATER USE (L)	CALORIES (g)	FAT (g)	CARBS (g)	PROTEIN (g)	CALCIUM** (mg)
DAIRY MILK*				148	8	12	8	270
RICE MILK				115	2,4	22,4	0,7	288
SOY MILK				105	3,6	12	6,4	300
ALMOND MILK				36,6	2,6	3,2	1	449
OAT MILK				120	5	16	3	350

0 0,2 0,4 0,6   0 0,5 1,0 1,5   0   40   80 120

*whole cow's milk
**most milks are fortified with calcium and other minerals and vitamins

Though store-bought, branded, plant-based milks are usually fortified with vitamins A, B12, and D as well as calcium, which is a great plus, dairy substitute can also be made at home. If you have the passion to experiment with this, it's often much more economical to make them yourself, and you can cater to your exact taste. You can experiment with the sweetness, flavor, and consistency you prefer; you can even customize your milk blends by adding cacao/berries or mixing coconut-almond milk, for example.

The Most Difficult Part of Being Vegan is Waking up at 5:00 a.m. to Milk the Almonds

Homemade Almond Milk

1 cup raw almonds (soaked overnight in cool water or 1–2 hours in very
   hot water)
5 cups water (less to thicken, more to thin)
1 pinch sea salt

OPTIONAL FLAVORS TO ADD IN:
Sweeten with 2 whole dates (or any other sweetener of choice)
Vanilla flavored with 1 tsp vanilla extract
Chocolate milk with 2 tbsp cocoa powder
Berry milk with ½ cup berries

Add your soaked almonds, water, salt, and any other optional add-ins to a
high-speed blender and blend until creamy and smooth. Keep it running for
at least one to two minutes so you get the most out of your almonds. Strain
using a nut milk bag. If you do not have one, you can try a thin dish towel.
Simply lay a clean dish towel over a mixing bowl, pour over the almond
milk, carefully gather the corners, and lift up. Then squeeze until all the liquid
is extracted. Discard pulp, or save for adding to baked goods like crackers.
Finally, transfer milk to a jar or a covered bottle and refrigerate. Will keep for
up to four to five days, though best when fresh. Shake well before drinking,
as it tends to separate.

Homemade Oat Milk

1 cup rolled oats
4 cups water

Add 1 cup rolled oats and 4 cups water to a high-speed blender and blend
on high for 30–45 seconds. Strain through a kitchen towel or a clean T-shirt
for best results as nut milk bags and fine mesh strainers often let out too much
pulp when making oat milk.

You can also decide to strain them twice to remove any excess starch, as that starch can lead to a more "slimy" texture. Keep in mind that soaking the oats or over-blending can also make the milk slimy. Well-sealed in the refrigerator, oat milk should last about five days.

Vegan Cheddar-like Cheese (Potato-Based)

2 cups potatoes

1 cup carrots

½ cup water

½ cup nutritional yeast

⅓ cup extra-virgin olive oil

1 tbsp lemon juice

1 tsp salt

Boil or steam the peeled and diced potatoes and carrots for about twenty minutes or until soft. Drain them and add them to a blender, add all the remaining ingredients and blend until smooth. Serve immediately with tortilla chips or as a dip, or use it to make pizza, lasagna, mac and cheese, or any other recipe that calls for cheese. Keep leftovers in a sealed container in the fridge for about four to five days.

Vegan Feta-like Cheese (Tofu-Based)

Firm tofu pack (450 g)

1 tbsp nutritional yeast

1 tbsp apple cider vinegar

1 tsp lemon juice

2 tbsp warm water

2 tbsp olive oil

1 tsp white miso (optional but recommended)

1 ¼ tsp salt

¼ tsp garlic powder (to taste)

Drain and press your tofu to get all of the excess liquid out of it. While the tofu is pressing, make a marinade. Add water, nutritional yeast, apple cider vinegar, lemon juice, miso, salt, and spices to a dish and give it all a stir with a fork. Crumble the tofu and add it to the marinade. Allow your tofu feta to sit in the fridge for at least an hour to let the tofu soak up the flavors. It will taste even better if it sits overnight. Feel free to season it with garlic or different herbs such as oregano or thyme.

Vegan Spreadable Cheese (Cashew-Based)

1 cup raw cashews soaked for at least 2 hours (or overnight), drained, and rinsed

2 tbsp nutritional yeast

2 tbsp freshly squeezed lemon juice

¼ cup water or more as needed

¼ tsp garlic powder (to taste)

½ tsp salt (to taste)

¼ tsp freshly ground black pepper (to taste)

Place all the ingredients, except the water, in a food processor and pulse repeatedly to break the cashews down, until they are coarse and well blended. Scrape the sides of the food processor down with a spatula. With the processor back on, drizzle in the water and let the cashews process for about ten seconds. Stop and scrape the machine down again. Continue processing for a full one to two minutes or until the cashew cheese is smooth and thick, adding a tablespoon of extra water if needed. The consistency should be a bit like hummus. Taste the cashew cheese, and add lemon, salt, and pepper to taste. If you like, pulse in fresh herbs or other flavorings. Cashew cheese will keep for up to six days in an airtight container in the fridge.

Vegan Stretchy Mozzarella-like Cheese (Cashew-Based)

½ cup raw cashews, soaked for at least 2 hours (or overnight), drained, and rinsed

1 cup water

3 tbsp + 2 tsp tapioca starch (also called tapioca flour)

1 tbsp nutritional yeast

1 tsp apple cider vinegar

½ tsp salt

¼ tsp garlic powder (optional)

Drain the cashews and add, along with all the remaining ingredients, to a blender. Blend until completely smooth. It will be very watery. Pour into a small saucepan over medium-high heat and stir continually. The cheese will start forming clumps; keep stirring until the mixture turns from watery to a thicker, melty, cheese sauce. This takes about five minutes. Serve hot or allow to cool by storing in an airtight container in the fridge for two to three days. The cheese will get thicker as it cools but will stay in a melty state.

EGGLESS IDEAS

The other day, I heard a twelve-year-old calling eggs the chicken's period. Gross pre-teen humor aside, chickens do have to go through a physically taxing process, especially modern hens who have been bred to produce such unnaturally high rates of eggs. Eggs can be easily replaced, especially when baking, to reduce demand and spare the lives of millions of male chicks who are deemed useless and killed every day in the egg industry.

Baking

Other than actual packaged "egg replacers," which you can pick up from the baking section or the vegan section at a specialty supermarket, there are some go-to tricks for your favorite recipes, made from ingredients you probably already have at home. If a recipe requires an egg, you can replace it with any of the items shown below.

1/4 cup applesauce

1/2 mashed banana

1/2 mashed avocado

1/4 cup cooked and puréed sweet potato, pumpkin, or squash

1 tbsp ground flaxseed or chia seed + 3 tbsp water (mix and allow 10 minutes to settle for an "egg-like" texture)

3 tbsp peanut butter (or any other nut butter)

1/4 cup vegan yogurt or blended silken tofu

1 tbsp vinegar or 2 tbsp lemon juice + 1 tbsp baking soda

2 tbsp potato starch or cornstarch +2 tbsp water

4 tbsp chickpea flour + 4 tbsp water

3 tbsp aquafaba*

*Aquafaba is the water that chickpeas have been soaked in, usually left over from a can or jar of chickpeas. If you whip it, it is perfect to replace egg whites in recipes including meringues, macaroons, and marshmallows.

Breakfast

If you are traditionally used to your eggs in the morning, this might be one of the hardest foods to give up. The next chapter includes great alternative breakfast ideas, including ones that are very similar in taste and texture to eggs, like chickpea omelets or simply scrambling tofu with a bit of turmeric and salt.

For me personally, tofu scramble has been a real game changer! It looks and tastes a lot like scrambled eggs, but it is also lower in fat and cholesterol-free, so it's a win-win! It's also loaded with protein and is easy to make—in less than five minutes. I make mine with crumbled, firm tofu and turmeric powder, salt, and ground black pepper to taste, but you can customize it with all the ingredients you'd use on your regular scrambled eggs, such as spinach, onions, plant-based cheese, nutritional yeast, tomatoes, or mushrooms.

Tofu Scramble

- Drain firm tofu and mash with a fork
- Cook over the stove
- Add tumeric, salt, and pepper
- Add any veggies you like
  (mushrooms, onion)

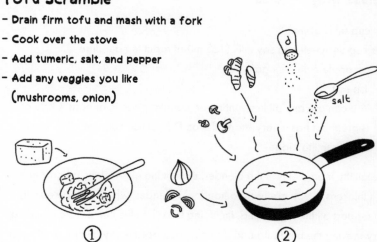

① ②

If you are feeling extra creative in the kitchen, there are also plenty of wild ideas out there, including egg yolk from tomatoes or mangoes. Some brands also offer yummy scramble mixes (sold as a yellow liquid in bottles or carton packs) that you can just pour into a frying pan, and they taste exactly like scrambled eggs.

Egg-free mayo

Egg-free mayo is becoming easier to find. I usually find it in specialty stores, in vegan-specific supermarket aisles, or in the healthy/organic section. Not only does it look and taste exactly like mayonnaise, but it tends to be lower in calories too! In case you couldn't find it, or you only found a brand that is too processed, or you are on a budget, an even better option to store-bought mayonnaise is making it yourself. Here is a simple four-ingredient recipe to make your own mayo at home:

Eggless Mayonnaise

> 1 cup oil (250 ml)*
> ½ cup unsweetened soy milk (125 ml) at room temperature
> 2 tsp apple cider vinegar
> ½ tsp salt
> * You can use any oil like sunflower, canola, peanut, or corn. Olive oil is great but has a very strong flavor. Do not use coconut oil as it will solidify in the fridge.

Place all the ingredients in the blender, except the oil. Add the oil gradually until it thickens. If you are using a handheld blender, which may be easier, you can add all the ingredients, including the oil, to the cup before blending, but try moving the blade up and down to incorporate any oil that is sitting at the top. Try the mayo and add more salt if needed. If it's too thick, you can add more milk, and if it is too watery, add more oil. Keep in mind that it will thicken further in the fridge.

Use it immediately or keep it in the fridge for a few hours until it is cold. Keep leftovers in an airtight container or a jar in the fridge for about four to seven days.

Note: If your mayo doesn't emulsify, you can add more oil until it thickens. It's really important that the milk and the oil are at the same temperature, so I find room temperature is best. You can also add other ingredients for flavor, like garlic (you'll get a delicious vegan aioli), chili oil, mustard, or maple syrup. It's also delicious with fresh or dried herbs like parsley or dill.

REPLACING MEAT

Believe it or not, when you think of biting into a big, juicy burger, you are not really craving the meat itself. You crave fat, flavor, salt, texture and familiarity. I say you don't actually crave meat because otherwise you would have had an instinctive tendency to jump on a grazing cow and bite it, or when you looked at a running chicken, your first thought would have been "oh yum!"

But the reality is that we have gotten so used to meat, and our favorite foods often include it. So, as you transition, be clear on the replacement of everything you eliminate, especially as you adjust your favorite recipes.

Here are some substitutes you can use in your classic recipes.

Everyday produce and pantry items as meat replacements

Many everyday items make for great substitutes in your favorite recipes, such as:

- **LENTILS:** Excellent for mincemeat-based recipes like bolognese sauce or lasagnas. Just cook and drain brown lentils, and use them in the pasta's tomato sauce recipe.
- **BLACK BEANS:** My go-to alternative for Mexican cuisine. They make great mincemeat alternatives in tacos and burrito bowls.
- **MUSHROOMS:** You can't go wrong with a great mushroom stroganoff or just grilling a large Portobello mushroom over a barbecue as a burger patty.
- **EGGPLANTS:** They are perfect for stews. I love cooked eggplant cubes with tomato sauce, served over rice.

Tofu

Tofu has been a staple in Asian vegetarian cuisines for centuries. It is a low-calorie source of protein that is not very strong in flavor, but it takes on the flavors of the other ingredients it is cooked with. That is why it is so versatile, as it easily absorbs aromas from spices and marinades. So it makes for a great addition in curries, on skewers during barbecues, and on salads.

Because tofu is a soy product, there is always concern about genetically modified organisms (GMOs), because the soybean is one of the most genetically engineered crops in the world, not just because of our high demand for the plant, but also because it is used extensively in animal feed. For that reason, try to choose organic soy products.

When shopping for tofu, you may find several different varieties, including silken, medium, firm, and extra-firm. The difference between them is primarily texture, which depends on how much of its water is pressed out. The best way to determine what variety of tofu to buy is knowing the way it will be prepared or cooked. Blocks of tofu are usually packed in tubs of water or sometimes vacuum-sealed and found in the refrigerated section of your grocery store.

- **SILKEN TOFU:** Silken tofu works well in creamy and blended foods like smoothies, desserts, puddings, salad dressings, sauces, and dips.
- **MEDIUM TOFU:** This tofu is denser than silken but still fairly delicate. It works well in gently simmered soups, like miso.
- **FIRM TOFU:** This tofu absorbs flavors well and can be stir-fried and pan-fried; it is also great when crumbled and used in tofu scrambles.
- **EXTRA-FIRM TOFU:** This is essentially considered the all-purpose tofu that holds its shape well and is excellent for slicing and cubing. It's an ideal choice for pan-frying, stir-frying, baking, grilling, and scrambling.

Cooking tofu

DRAIN: Regardless of which variety you pick, tofu contains a fair amount of liquid, and it's helpful to remove as much as possible before cooking, which makes a big difference in the finished texture of the tofu—it ensures that it is soft and chewy rather than soggy.

PRESS: To prepare it, place the tofu, as a whole block or cut into large cubes, in between a few layers of paper towels and weigh it down with something heavy. Try to leave it pressed for about twenty minutes. Many varieties are pre-drained and pre-pressed; if they are, you can skip this part.

MARINATE: On its own, tofu is rather neutral tasting and very mildly flavored. But it has a sponge-like ability to soak up marinades, which makes it a very interesting canvas to work with. Firm and extra-firm tofu have the best results with marinating, since they can be relied on to keep their shape. After you press and drain the tofu, soak it in any marinade for at least thirty minutes before cooking. There are plenty of marinade options out there, including spicy barbecue flavors, sweet teriyaki, and lemon herb, among others. Here is an example of a simple marinade for around 275 g/10 oz of firm tofu, but feel free to experiment:

> 2 tbsp soy sauce or tamari sauce
> 1 tbsp apple cider vinegar or rice vinegar
> 1 tbsp maple syrup
> 2 garlic cloves, minced, or 1 tsp garlic powder
> 2 tsp cornstarch (optional)
> 1 tbsp sesame oil (optional)
> Extra-virgin olive oil to taste (optional)

FRY, BAKE, OR GRILL: Once your tofu is ready, it's time to cook it! And just as there are an infinite number of ways to flavor tofu, the same goes for cooking.

- **Stir-fried/pan-fried:** This is the easiest way to cook tofu. It comes out crispy without deep frying. Cut into cubes, sticks, or wedges, and just sauté in a frying pan or wok. For extra crispiness, toss it with cornstarch until all the pieces are well-coated before cooking. The tofu comes out of the wok with super-crisp, golden edges and a soft, chewy center. For best results, start with extra-firm or firm tofu, and press out as much water as possible before cooking.
- **Baked:** When eaten straight from the oven, baked tofu has an irresistibly crispy outside and a creamy, soft middle. And even though it loses its crispness once cooled, it becomes wonderfully firm and chewy. Whether you bake it plain or soak it in a marinade first, you can toss baked tofu over just about everything, from salads to tacos and noodle dishes.

- **Grilled:** Cooking tofu kebab-style on the grill is great for when you want to barbecue outdoors and serve skewers. The secret to success with grilled tofu is starting with extra-firm tofu, freezing it first for a denser texture—which will also help it soak up even more marinade or barbecue sauce—and cutting the block into generous one-inch cubes or larger. The skewers will cook in under ten minutes, and it's best to turn them regularly.
- **Scrambled:** Scrambled tofu has a texture similar to scrambled eggs, is just as versatile, and is infinitely customizable. For the basic version, just add turmeric for a yellow, egg-like color. Eat tofu scrambled on its own, add cooked vegetables, stuff it in a pita, or add it to your avocado toast.

Tempeh

If you are lucky enough to find tempeh in your local supermarket, grab it! Tempeh is a soy product like tofu, but while tofu is made from soy milk, tempeh is made using the whole soybean, so it has a different nutritional profile. It contains even more protein, fiber, and vitamins than tofu. Additionally, as a fermented food, it also contains prebiotics, which may improve digestive health and reduce inflammation. It also has a more distinct flavor than tofu and a meaty, firm texture.

Cooking tempeh

Baking is my favorite method to cook tempeh. It's really easy, and the nutty cubes become crisp and caramelized while they're in the oven.

CHOP AND STEAM: Cut into cubes and steam for ten minutes. Try not to skip the steaming, because it helps soak up a marinade and infuses it with extra flavors.

MARINATE: Just like with tofu, you can experiment with marinades for the flavor you need. Try to let the cubes soak for at least thirty minutes. A simple marinade is:

¼ cup tamari
2 tbsp rice vinegar
2 tbsp maple syrup
1 tbsp extra-virgin olive oil
1 tsp sriracha (optional)
Freshly ground black pepper

BAKE: Spread the marinated cubes on a parchment-lined baking sheet, and bake them for about twenty minutes until the cubes are charred around the edges. You can remove them halfway through, brush some extra marinade and place them back in.

Jackfruit

This fruit is one of my personal favorites. Jackfruit is a relative of figs and breadfruit that grows in tropical areas of Southeast Asia, Brazil, and Africa. While it is technically a fruit, its consistency is similar to that of chicken or "pulled meat." It has a fairly neutral taste when young and before it ripens, so it takes on the flavor of whatever sauce or seasoning you pair it with. It has a stringy consistency that works especially well with tangy barbecue sauce or in sandwiches, stir-fries, curries, tacos, and burritos.

While it is a great meat replacement, unlike animal meat, jackfruit contains no saturated fat or cholesterol; it is light in sodium, packed with heart-healthy nutrients, and low in calories.

The best way to buy young, unripe jackfruit is either canned or in pouches. This is the type that is gaining a lot of attention as a meat alternative. You may also find a whole green jackfruit in the produce section, but unless you are an avid DIYer, it might get too messy as it would be filled with a sticky, white resin that stains whatever it gets on. So I would stay away from that at first.

Cooking jackfruit

Young jackfruit is generally packed with some water, and sometimes also with salt, so give it a good rinse with cold water, and let it drain in a colander before using it in recipes. Then you can literally do anything with it. It works especially well with bold and spicy flavors. The Mexican-food lover and the Middle Eastern blood in me make jackfruit my go-to option for quesadillas and shawarma cravings. All you need to do is just add some spices (I use fajita spices, a shawarma spice blend, or a shish-taouk mix) and just sauté over the stove.

Packaged meat alternatives

You can, of course, find packaged meat alternatives in the freezer section of your grocery store. From minced "meat" and burger patties to "chicken" nuggets and even "fish" fillets, it has become exponentially easier to just pick up a vegetable-based substitute typically made up of a combination of beans, grains, vegetables, and spices. Many of these products may be processed, but if your objective is to satisfy a craving (versus purely live on greens), then go for it. I believe that, in moderation, as long as they are enabling your transition, they would still be a better alternative to meat.

Two years ago, I invited a group of new work colleagues over for a barbecue. Of course, I knew a few of them wouldn't be happy knowing I meant a fully vegan barbecue. So, I didn't disclose the menu. I just grilled some Beyond Meat burger patties, which are plant-based but look exactly like regular cow-meat patties. When the first batch was done, they sat down and started devouring them while discussing how great this gathering was and how much they loved the food. At that point, I was still standing by the grill, flipping more patties as they ate. I finally joined them and as I sat down and started layering my burger, I could see, from the corner of my eye, that everyone was looking at me and thinking, "What is she doing?" As soon as I took the first bite, one of them screamed, "But, Assile! You don't eat meat!" With a cheeky smile, I said, "This isn't meat." Everyone's jaw dropped. Perhaps if I had said something earlier, it would have been easy to tell the difference between a Beyond Burger patty and a beef patty. But the reality is that they are equally enjoyable, so when I kept it a secret, no one questioned it. Now, moral code aside for my little white lie, the reality is that this story is a great example of how easy it is to make the switch. Many of my colleagues went on to tell family and friends about how they can get the same "barbecue experience" with less saturated fat and no cholesterol, while sparing a life and saving the planet too! Beyond Meat is not the only company out there offering such great alternatives. Many others, including Impossible, Moving Mountains, and Meatless Farm, have developed recipes so close to what society is used to eating that not many people can tell the difference.

Below is a comparison of a quarter-pound beef patty with the famous plant-based Beyond Burger:

THE BEYOND BURGER

ANIMAL-BASED BEEF

VS

THE BEYOND BURGER		ANIMAL-BASED BEEF
20	PROTEIN (G)	19
25%	IRON (DV)	12%
5	SATURATED FAT (G)	9
O	CHOLESTEROL (MG)	80
22	TOTAL FAT (G)	23
290	CALORIES	287
✓	PLANT-BASED	✗
✓	ANTIBIOTIC-FREE	?
✓	HORMONE-FREE	?
✓	GMO-FREE	?
99%	LESS WATER	
93%	LESS LAND	
90%	FEWER GHGE	
46%	LESS ENERGY	

NUTRITIONAL CONSIDERATIONS

As I mentioned in Chapter 2, I would recommend that you check out *The China Study*, one of the longest and most comprehensive books on nutritional studies which examines the link between the consumption of animal products and chronic illnesses and explains how you do not need animal products for a healthy and balanced diet. In fact, you don't only survive, but can thrive without them. But if you are still worried about the fact that Nana has always said, "Eat meat, *habibi*; you need iron," or that your old high school basketball coach used to tell you, "Eat three chicken breasts after the game for them protein, bub," below are some thoughts to keep in mind.

Protein-rich foods

With adequate caloric intake and a varied diet, a plant-based diet can easily meet the recommendations for protein intake, regardless of age, gender, or level of physical activity. Protein-packed foods include legumes (e.g., peas, beans, lentils, chickpeas—yum hummus, fava beans, lupin beans, and so on), soy and soy products (tofu, edamame, tempeh, soymilk, yogurt, and so on), seitan (made of hydrated gluten, which is the main protein of wheat and has a very meaty texture), and quinoa. Nuts, seeds, grains, and vegetables also provide varying amounts of protein.

As I mentioned earlier, healthy adults require approximately 0.8 grams of protein per kilogram of body weight each day, regardless of gender. This means that a man weighing 70 kg (154 lb) needs to consume approximately 60 grams (~2 oz) of protein per day (70 x 0.8 = 60). Meanwhile, a woman weighing 60 kg (132 lb) requires 48 grams (1.7 oz). Athletes might require more protein, but with proper planning, they too can easily obtain all the protein they need from a vegan diet.

On the next page, you'll find some examples of the average amounts of protein in plant-based food. In addition to providing suitable amounts of protein, plant-based foods come with added benefits, as they are low in fat and sodium and high in fiber, minerals, and vitamins. One cup of cooked lentils, for example, contains 18 grams of protein, which is the same amount of protein in three eggs, and provides 30 percent and 37 percent of the daily protein requirements for men and women, respectively.

Where Do I Get My Protein From?

Green beans
2 cups (240g)
80 kcal
4g protein

Peas
1 cup (160g)
134 kcal
9g protein

Lentils
1 cup (198g)
230 kcal
18g protein

Chickpeas
1 cup (200g)
269 kcal
15g protein

Kidney beans
1 cup (177g)
225 kcal
15.3g protein

Seitan
100 g
143 kcal
19g protein

Tempeh
1 cup (166g)
320 kcal
34g protein

Edamame
1 cup (155g)
189 kcal
17g protein

Tofu
½ Cup (100g)
94 kcal
10g protein

Soybeans
1 cup (172g)
296 kcal
31.3g protein

Barley
1 cup (157g)
193 kcal
3.5g protein

Quinoa
1 cup (185g)
222 kcal
8g protein

Farro
1 cup (150g)
200 kcal
8g protein

Freekeh
1/2 cup (80g)
260 kcal
16g protein

Bulgur
1 cup (182g)
151 kcal
6g protein

Asparagus
2 cups (360g)
76 kcal
8.5g protein

Spinach, cooked
2 cups (360g)
97 kcal
12g protein

Broccoli
3 cups (270g)
92 kcal
7.6g protein

Artichoke
1 cup (170g)
90 kcal
5g protein

Brown rice
1 cup (195g)
238 kcal
5.3g protein

Peanut butter
2 tbsp (32g)
190 kcal
7.2g protein

Almonds
½ cup (60g)
340 kcal
12g protein

Pumpkin seeds
3 tbsp (30g)
160 kcal
7g protein

Chia seeds
3 tbsp (39g)
180 kcal
6g protein

Flaxseeds
3 tbsp (31g)
170 kcal
6g protein

Nutritional yeast
1 tbsp (9g)
34 kcal
5g protein

Soy milk
1 cup (224ml)
105 kcal
6.4g protein

Tahini
2 tbsp (32g)
210 kcal
8g protein

Quick oats
½ cup (40g)
150 kcal
5g protein

All legumes and grains mentioned above are per cooked/boiled serving

Iron-rich foods

Who Should We Be Eating Like?

Iron is an important mineral that is required to prevent iron deficiency anemia, a common nutrient deficiency, and it is particularly important for women at fertility age, pregnant women, adolescents, and athletes who have higher iron requirements.

When I was in high school and throughout my twenties, I had anemia, and I remember constantly feeling sleepy and tired. After changing my lifestyle and moving to a healthy, plant-based diet, my iron levels are actually on the high side! This always surprises everyone, because many people think that red meat is the only source of iron. However plant-based foods can be very rich in iron, and it can be relatively easy to get all the iron you need if you are eating the right foods.

Some iron-rich foods include pulses and legumes (beans, lentils, peas), nuts, and seeds (tahini from sesame seeds is a great source; are we all agreeing that hummus is everything?), tofu, whole and fortified grains, leafy greens (think Popeye, the sailor man, and those cans of spinach), dried fruits like apricots, prunes, figs, and raisins, and green vegetables like broccoli and okra.

Iron in Plant-Based Foods

Cereal, complete all bran*
0.75 cup (30g)
92 kcal
18 mg iron

Kidney beans
1 cup (177g)
225 kcal
5.2 mg iron

Spinach, cooked
2 cups (360g)
97 kcal
10.5 mg iron

Chia seeds
3 tbsp (39g)
180 kcal
3.2 mg iron

Barley
1 cup (157g)
193 kcal
2.4 mg iron

Soybeans
1 cup (172g)
296 kcal
8.84 mg iron

Lentils
1 cup (198g)
230 kcal
6.59 mg iron

Asparagus
2 cups (360g)
76 kcal
8.2 mg iron

Pumpkin seeds
3 tbsp (30g)
160 kcal
4.5 mg iron

Quinoa
1 cup (185g)
222 kcal
2.76 mg iron

Tempeh
1 cup (166g)
320 kcal
4.5 mg iron

Peas
1 cup (160g)
134 kcal
2.4 mg iron

Potato, baked
1 large (400g)
372 kcal
1.4 mg iron

Tahini
2 tbsp (32g)
210 kcal
2.7 mg iron

Dark chocolate, 70—85%
1 serving (28 g)
170 kcal
3.4 mg iron

Chickpeas
1 cup (200g)
269 kcal
4.74 mg iron

Green beans
2 cups (240g)
80 kcal
3mg iron

Hearts of palm
1 cup (146g)
41 kcal
4.6 mg iron

Sesame seeds
2 tbsp (18g)
104 kcal
2.6 mg iron

Dried apricots
10 pieces (80g)
200 kcal
2.2 mg iron

Edamame
1 cup (155g)
189 kcal
1.7 mg iron

Broccoli
3 cups (270g)
92 kcal
2 mg iron

Mulberries
1 cup (140g)
60 kcal
2.6 mg iron

Olives
1 cup (135g)
157 kcal
8.5 mg iron

Prune juice
1 cup (256ml)
182 kcal
3 mg iron

*store bought, branded, fortified
All legumes and grains mentioned above are per cooked/boiled serving

Adults need approximately 8.7 mg of iron per day, and it goes up to 14.8 mg for women during their menstrual cycles. This varies across life stages like pregnancy, breastfeeding, childhood, and the teenage years, but I am sharing a rough average to show that it is relatively easy to get the recommended intake from everyday healthy foods.

Some tips to improve iron absorption include:

ADD A VITAMIN C SOURCE TO YOUR MEAL: Adding vitamin C helps iron absorption, especially when it comes to leafy greens like spinach, which makes lemon juice on top of a salad or on cooked spinach a great idea. Fresh fruits and vegetables such as kiwi fruits, oranges, pineapples, strawberries, bell peppers, broccoli, cabbage, and tomatoes are also all great sources of vitamin C.

SOAK YOUR LEGUMES AND WHOLE GRAINS: Soaking not only shortens cooking times, but also improves iron absorption by reduction of phytic acid.

AVOID TEA, COFFEE, AND COCOA DURING YOUR MEAL: Try to wait for at least an hour after your meal before drinking caffeinated beverages. Or maybe just avoid them altogether before they become addictive.

Vitamin B 12

Essential for the formation of red blood cells, vitamin B 12 is key for the brain and nervous system formation. We used to get enough B 12 through our fruits and veggies, but thanks to modern agriculture and its impact on the soil, where the B 12 producing bacteria live, it is now difficult for us to get B 12.

It's widely said that vitamin B12 is only found in animal sources, but the reality is that fortified breakfast cereals and some low-salt yeast extracts contain B12, as do fortified plant-milks, cereals, and soy products. Some people cringe at the idea of having to resort to fortified foods for B12, but whether you eat meat or not, the majority of your B12 intake is most probably coming from fortified sources anyways.

You can also choose to take a B12 supplement. I tend to depend on bloodwork before supplementing, so ideally, check if you need it, and then go for it. However, B12 deficiency is a serious health issue, so if you do not have the means to check via a blood test, you can choose to take good plant-based supplements just in case.

CHAPTER 6

EASY PEASY LEMON SQUEEZY

Meal prep with less than five main ingredients

Learning a New Vegan Recipe

It is hard enough transitioning into a whole new lifestyle. The last thing you would want is for it to be complicated. I am a full-time working mother juggling a demanding corporate job, running my own business, helping with homework, working out every day, and actively campaigning for healthy living, animal rights, and environmental consciousness, so I don't have much time in the kitchen either. I get it.

In this chapter, I will share some of the easiest and quickest meal ideas that I have either come across or developed along this journey.

Plant-based cooking is remarkably easy to learn, and you'll invariably eat fresher, tastier meals made with higher quality ingredients. As your cooking skills develop, you may also grow to love the calming, meditative time spent in the kitchen, doing simple tasks like steaming rice or chopping vegetables.

If you love spending time in the kitchen and experimenting with new flavors and textures, you might find this to be your favorite part of a vegan journey. I have had several friends discover their passion for cooking while they went through this process, as it opens the doors to unexplored food territory. But just in case you don't find cooking enjoyable, I have made sure that all the ideas below are not sophisticated recipes but more of "food combinations," so that they are easy to whip up with a few everyday ingredients and can be ready in minutes.

SHORTCUTS AND TIPS

FREEZE BANANAS: Whenever your bananas are getting too ripe, just peel them and keep them in a bag in the freezer. They always come in handy in smoothies, frozen fruit bowls, or for "nice"-cream. You can do the same with any other fruit and vegetable that you are not consuming before it goes bad. I freeze unused fresh strawberries, green beans, berries, and mangos, to name a few.

PRESOAKED BEANS AND CHICKPEAS: Beans and chickpeas are harder to cook as they require soaking and may be hard to digest if not soaked right. This is also time-consuming and requires you to plan for the meal beforehand. So although I try to avoid canned products, canned legumes or those sold in a glass jar are easier to work with—and digest—as they are already soaked and cooked and just need to be heated.

CACAO VS. COCOA: Look for cacao, not cocoa. In one sense, the two words mean the same thing, as "cocoa" is the English adaptation of the word "cacao." However, there are also important distinctions between the two. A product labeled *cacao* comes straight from the raw cacao beans, meaning it is closer to its original form, with minimal processing and no additives while what is called *cocoa* is made of beans that have been roasted and often processed.

DATES AND NUTS are great on-the-go snacks. Always plan to have some in case you don't find time to prepare a snack. Dates make an amazingly nutritious snack. They are sweet enough to satisfy sugar cravings and are especially great as a pre-gym snack. Try dipping dates in tahini or in peanut butter.

FREEZE EVERYDAY COOKING ITEMS like leftover chopped herbs, such as cilantro/coriander, peeled garlic, or chopped onions. You can even freeze lemon juice in ice-cube trays. When you need to use these items for cooking, just throw them into the pot.

HEALTHIER BREAD HACKS: Experiment with ways to use vegetables as alternatives to bread. Use lettuce leaves as burger buns or as sandwich wraps, in place of pita or tortilla bread. For example, you can try quinoa and diced artichoke lettuce wraps. Another idea is to use baked sweet potatoes as a base instead of toast. Cut the sweet potatoes into circles or lengthwise into large slices and roast them in the oven. You can serve them as the base for avocado-toast or chickpea "tuna" salad.

BREAKFAST IDEAS

Tofu and Anything Scrambled Eggs

1 pack firm tofu
1 tsp turmeric powder
Any veggies you usually add to eggs (spinach, mushroom, onion)
Nutritional yeast to taste (optional)
Salt/pepper to taste

Drain and press tofu, crumble it into a pan, and sauté. Add turmeric for color. Stir in veggies. Add salt and pepper to taste. You can also add nutritional yeast for a "cheesy" omelet flavor.

So Many Flavors of Overnight Oats

½ cup rolled oats
½ cup any plant-based milk
1 tbsp sweetener like maple syrup, brown sugar, or agave syrup
Your favorite fruits (berries or bananas)
Cacao powder, peanut butter, cinnamon, chia seeds (optional)

Fill half a jar with oats, and top it off with plant-based milk and a sweetener of choice. Add any optional flavors like peanut butter, chia seeds, and/or cacao powder. You can also add bananas overnight if you like them extra soggy. Keep in the fridge overnight or around five hours. Top with fruits, granola, or seeds.

Two-Way Chickpeas

   1 cup cooked chickpeas (soaked and boiled or as is, if using jar or can)
   3 tbsp soy yogurt or 1 tbsp olive oil
   1 tbsp cumin
   Salt to taste
   Toasted pita bread (optional)

Heat the chickpeas over the stove with some water until soft and warm.
Drain. Add salt and cumin to taste. Top with soy yogurt. You can add toasted
pita bread for an Arabic-style "fatteh" dish, or you can ditch the yogurt and
bread and just add extra-virgin olive oil to turn into "balila."

Homemade Granola

*Easy cereal alternative to serve with milk or with coconut yogurt, topped
with fruits.*

   4 cups rolled oats
   ½ cup maple syrup
   ½ cup olive oil
   Seeds (chia, sesame)
   ½ tsp cinnamon and/or cacao powder
   Vegan chocolate chips (optional)

In a bowl, mix oats with maple syrup and oil. Taste to check how sweet
you like them, and add or reduce the maple syrup accordingly. Add cacao
powder and/or cinnamon for extra flavor. Add seeds to your liking. Lay
on baking paper on a flat tray, try to flatten the oats to make sure they get
evenly cooked, and place in oven at 180°C/350°F for twenty to twenty-
five minutes until golden-brown.

*Optional: You can add in vegan chocolate chips five minutes before
removing from oven.*

Pancakes

With a toddler in the house, almost every day is pancake day. After many attempts, I realized that you can basically turn anything into a pancake if you have any powdered flour and an equal ratio of liquid. Then it's just a matter of adding extra flavor.

½ cup whole wheat flour (or any flour)
½ cup plant-based milk (oat, soy, or almond work best)
½ tsp baking powder
1 tsp oil for cooking
1 tbsp brown sugar (optional, best to go without it and top with maple syrup to sweeten instead)
½ tsp vanilla, spirulina, or cacao powder (optional)

Mix all the ingredients with a handheld blender. I like to add green spirulina for color or cacao powder for chocolate pancakes. Heat cooking oil on a pan or skillet over the stove and, while on low heat, pour some of the pancake mix into the pan to make one pancake at a time. When you see it begin to form little bubbles, it's time to flip it over. I like to add banana slices or blueberries before flipping it as well. Top with peanut butter or chocolate spread.

Avocado Toast

Sourdough bread, baked sweet potato slice, or any toast
Avocado
Salt
Olive oil
Chili flakes (optional)

Get your toast nice and warm. Smash avocado over it with a fork. Top with lots of olive oil and salt to taste. I love adding chili flakes for an extra kick and topping it with sliced cherry tomatoes.

Chickpea Omelet

¼ cup chickpea flour

⅓ cup water

1 tbsp nutritional yeast

¼ tsp salt

Veggies of choice (tomatoes, onions, peppers, mushrooms, zucchini, broccoli . . .)

Mix chickpea flour, nutritional yeast, salt, and water, and stir until there are no lumps. Meanwhile, dice up about ¼ cup of whatever veggies you want to add to your omelet, and sauté them on medium heat until they become tender, then place them on the side.

Turn up the heat to medium, and pour the batter in the skillet like you would a large pancake, and cook for about five minutes, until the top of the omelet no longer looks wet. Carefully loosen up the omelet with a spatula, flip it to the other side, and cook for three to five more minutes until it is no longer soft in the middle. Place the veggies on the omelet, and fold over so they are served as fillings in the middle.

Chia Pudding

2 tbsp chia seeds
½ cup plant-based milk (coconut milk works great here)
1 tsp any sweetener (maple syrup, agave syrup, date syrup)
Fruits of choice for topping (berries and bananas work great)

Fill the jar with chia seeds and cover with plant-based milk. Mix well and let it settle for two to three minutes, then mix again very well until you see no clumping. Cover the jar and store in fridge overnight or for at least two hours. When you're ready to eat it, top with your favorite fruit and enjoy cold!

Not-So-Classic PB&J

This is my go-to breakfast when traveling; I shamelessly carry around a jar of my favorite peanut butter to hotel breakfast buffets.

Cracker or slice of toast
1 tbsp peanut butter (or any other nut butter like almond butter)
Fresh berries of choice
Bananas
Chia seeds

Simply spread the peanut butter and top with your favorite choices. Many people like to add jelly, but I prefer to just use fresh berries to get the "jam-like" flavor when biting into it, without the added sugar. Make sure you pick a brand of peanut butter with no added sugar, or make your own by just throwing some dry-roasted peanuts in a food processor.

Smoothies and Green Juices

The best on-the-go breakfasts are smoothies and juices. In Chapter 3, we discussed the difference between the two, and I shared some of my favorite juice recipes. Smoothies are more filling and are typically meal replacements as they are denser in calories than juices. Here are some of my favorite smoothie recipes, but remember, the combinations are endless. You would need a blender, a combination of fruits (ideally frozen) and vegetables, and any liquid such as plant-based milk or coconut water. Have fun experimenting!

CHOCOLATY SMOOTHIE:

1 cup plant-based milk

1 tbsp peanut butter

1 tbsp cacao powder

½ frozen banana

2 pitted dates

FRUITY SMOOTHIE:

1 cup plant-based milk or coconut water

1 frozen banana

1 cup frozen fruits (any work; I like mixing strawberries and blueberries)

1 cup spinach (optional, to fit in some greens)

AVOCADO SMOOTHIE:

1 cup plant-based milk

½ ripe avocado

1 banana (frozen would be great!)

1 cup fresh spinach

1 tbsp peanut/almond butter

MANGO SMOOTHIE:

1 cup frozen mango

1 orange, sliced

2 frozen bananas

¼ cup orange juice, plus more if smoothie is too thick

Frozen Fruit Bowls and Açaí

I discovered these in Bali, and they became my new obsession. Frozen fruit bowls are essentially smoothies with less liquid, so you can serve them in a bowl with toppings instead of as a drink. This works with frozen bananas plus any frozen fruits. Just use any of the previous smoothie recipes with less liquid to get an ice-cream-like texture. One popular frozen fruit bowl is açaí. Açaí berries are round fruits that grow on açaí palm trees in the rainforests of Central and South America and are typically sold as frozen puree.

1 packet of frozen açaí puree

¼ cup of plant-based milk or coconut water (check açaí pack label, as brands may recommend different measurements)

1 banana (ideally frozen)

Toppings of choice (cut fruits, nuts, seeds, granola, coconut flakes, peanut butter)

Blend açaí puree with liquid of choice and banana in a blender or food processor. Serve with toppings of choice.

SNACK IDEAS

Sweet Snacks

"No-Tella" Homemade Hazelnut Spread

    2 cups hazelnuts
    ⅓ cup cacao powder
    ¾ cup maple syrup (more/less to taste)
    ½ cup plant-based milk
    1 tbsp vanilla extract
    2 tsp oil (optional)
    ¼ tsp salt (optional)

Roast the hazelnuts for fifteen minutes in the oven at 180°C/375°F. Once they are cooled, rub them so the skin comes off, and place them in a food processor. Pulse and add in all the ingredients. You can keep adding maple syrup slowly based on your preferred taste. If the texture is too thick, slowly add in ¼ cup of water (or more if needed) while blending for desired consistency. Keep blending until you get the desired texture; this may take a while depending on the size/power of your food processor.

Peanut Butter Banana Sandwich Bites

    3 bananas, ripe but still firm
    ¼ cup peanut butter (or nut butter of choice)

Slice bananas into circles. Spoon a bit of peanut butter on half of the banana slices, and top with the other half to create little peanut butter sandwich bites. Freeze for two hours, and serve frozen.

The Cleanest Ever Hot Chocolate

I don't drink coffee, so this is basically my "comfort" drink. It's a perfect warm drink for cloudy mornings, but its smooth and dark flavor makes it a great afternoon booster as well.

> 1 cup plant-based milk (I use oat milk for this)
> 1 tsp raw cacao (remember to try to find cacao, not cocoa)

Warm plant-based milk over the stove on low heat; use a sieve to sprinkle the cacao into the milk. Continue to stir very well over low heat until the cacao fully dissolves, ideally with a small whisk, and the hot chocolate is warm enough. If this is too bitter for your taste, you can add a sweetener like carob powder, agave syrup, or coconut sugar.

Salade de Fruit (Fruit Salad)

Growing up, my brother and I ate this almost every single day, because my mom somehow made us believe that it was the world's fanciest dish. Perhaps because she always said it in French, "Salade de fruit," or because it used to include a new seasonal fruit surprise every once in a while, this was always the perfect snack.

> Any fruits you have around! What I find work best are apples, bananas, kiwis, grapes, strawberries, blueberries, raspberries, mangos, and papayas.
> Fresh squeezed orange juice
> 1 tsp orange blossom water (optional, but makes a big difference)
> 1 tsp chia seeds (optional)

Cut up fruits, and pour juice blend (orange juice + orange blossom water) over them. You may top with chia seeds. This is best served fresh.

Date Brownies

2 cups pitted dates
½ cup peanut butter
½ cup cacao powder
¼ cup warm water

Mix dates and water in a food processor until a paste is formed. You may need a bit more (or less) water to get a sticky texture, depending on the type of dates. Add peanut butter and cacao powder and blend. You will end up with a sticky, paste-like mixture. Spread into a silicone baking tray ideally, and bake for fifteen minutes at 160°C/320°F. Allow it to cool before serving.

"Nice"-Cream

Though it has become easy to get store-bought, dairy-free ice cream, "nice"-cream, which is basically blended frozen bananas, is a healthier, low-calorie alternative with a great creamy texture.

2 frozen bananas
1 tsp cacao powder
2 pitted dates
1 tbsp plant-based milk or water (less or more, depending on desired texture)
1 tsp peanut butter (optional)
1 tsp carob molasses or agave syrup (optional sweeteners)

Blend and enjoy! You may want to add more or less liquid for texture. I love chocolate nice-cream, but you can flavor this any way you like, by adding frozen strawberries or mixed berries, for example.

The Best Ever Chocolate Cake

This is by no means "healthy." It's basically just sugar and flour, and I am not proud of its nutritional value. But sometimes, if a birthday party is coming up and I'm asked to bring the cake, I quickly bake this because everyone absolutely loves it, and it's so easy to make. So with the big disclaimer of please don't eat this every day, here is the recipe:

3 cups flour

½ cup cacao powder

2 cups sugar

2 tsp baking soda

2 tsp vanilla extract (optional but yummy)

2 tbsp vinegar (or lemon juice)

2 cups water

⅓ cup oil

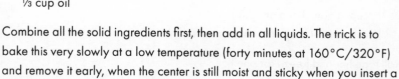

Combine all the solid ingredients first, then add in all liquids. The trick is to bake this very slowly at a low temperature (forty minutes at 160°C/320°F) and remove it early, when the center is still moist and sticky when you insert a toothpick. You can also add a frosting to this.

The Best Ever Chocolate Frosting

2 tbsp cacao

6 tbsp maple syrup

6 tbsp peanut butter

1 tsp vanilla extract

Mix all the ingredients, and spread over the cooled cake. This is a very sweet frosting. I personally prefer the cake without it and with a scoop of vanilla ice cream instead, but most dessert lovers like it with the frosting.

Energy Balls

I try to make energy balls in batches and store them in airtight containers. They make for great on-the-go snacks, especially for when I am late to the gym. There are endless possibilities here. You just need to figure out a sort of crunch to hold the ball together (like oats or nuts) and a sticky base (like dates or peanut butter). Then you can just experiment with the combinations to taste. Here are some of my favorites:

Oat Balls

  1 cup rolled oats
  ⅓ cup maple syrup
  ½ cup flaxseed meal
  ½ cup vegan chocolate chips
  ½ cup peanut butter (or any nut butter)

Roll together and freeze for one hour.

Chocolate Peanut Butter Date Balls

  ⅔ cup rolled oats
  3 tbsp peanut butter
  1 cup pitted dates (if dry, soak in warm water for ten minutes, then drain)
  ¼ cup vegan dark chocolate
  1 tbsp chia seeds (or flax seeds)

Pulse pitted dates in a food processor, then add oats, chocolate, chia seeds, and peanut butter, and continue mixing until combined. Depending on the desired texture, they should be consistently mixed without over-processing. Roll into balls, using your hands to mold them together. Freeze for fifteen minutes.

Smooth Date Balls

    1 cup pitted dates
    1 tbsp rose water
    1 tbsp orange blossom water
    Sesame and/or chia seeds for coating

Mix dates, rose water, and orange blossom water in a pot, and place on stove over low heat for five minutes. Make sure you remove the seeds from the dates first. Once they start to become sticky, pour mixture into a food processor to form a paste. With wet hands, roll mixture into balls, then coat with seeds. Optional variations include coating with cacao powder or mixing nuts into the food processor for a crunchier texture.

⌀●●

Savory Snacks

Spread Anything on Rice Cakes

My favorite office snack is usually the pack of rice cakes I keep in my locker with any type of spread: peanut butter and chia seeds, jam and bananas, homemade hazelnut spread. The easiest, I find, is zaatar (thyme) spread. Along with the rice cakes, I always keep dried thyme mixed with sesame seeds and a bottle of olive oil in my locker.

    Rice cake
    1 tbsp olive oil
    1 tsp zaatar (dried thyme, can be mixed with sesame seeds and/or dried
        sumac herb)

Mix the zaatar with olive oil and spread over rice cake. Can be served with cucumbers and cherry tomatoes.

Popcorn with "Nooch"

If you like cheese-flavored popcorn you will love this! Many people I know (who are not even vegan) sneak a pack of nutritional yeast or "nooch" into the movies to sprinkle on their theater-bought popcorn. Yes, yes, this is life changing.

Popcorn kernels
Oil for cooking
Salt
Nutritional yeast

The trick with well-popped popcorn is to get the temperature of the pot right. Use a large pot with a lid and add just a little bit of oil—enough to get the base lightly covered. Set the stove on medium to high heat and cover the pot. Add one kernel and once it pops, turn the stove setting to low heat (this is important to make sure you don't burn them) and add the rest of the popcorn. Don't put too much in one pot—just enough so that every kernel is touching the base. Add salt, cover, and wait. The popcorn is ready when you stop hearing any popping sounds. Sprinkle nutritional yeast generously and enjoy. You can also add a bit of olive oil over the popped popcorn if you like the taste; it will help the nutritional yeast stick for an extra cheesy flavor.

●●

Veggies and Dip

An easy snack is veggie sticks with any kind of dip. For veggies, you can use a mix of cucumbers, carrots, colored bell peppers, celery, and lettuce. Here are a few easy dips:

Hummus

1 ½ cups cooked chickpeas, drained

3 tbsp fresh lemon juice

5 tbsp tahini

2 tbsp extra-virgin olive oil, plus more for serving

½ tsp ground cumin

2–3 tbsp water (depends on desired thickness)

1 small garlic clove, minced (optional)

Salt to taste

A dash of ground paprika or sumac for serving (optional)

In the bowl of a food processor, combine the chickpeas, tahini and lemon juice, and process for one minute, scrape the sides and bottom of the bowl, then process for thirty seconds more. This extra time helps "whip" or "cream" the tahini, making the hummus smooth and creamy. Add the rest of the ingredients and process until thick and quite smooth. If the hummus is too thick, you can slowly add 2 to 3 tablespoons of water until you reach the perfect consistency. Taste for salt, and adjust as needed. Serve hummus with a drizzle of olive oil and a dash of sumac or paprika.

Avocado Dip

2 avocados

1 clove garlic (crushed)

1 tbsp freshly squeezed lemon juice

¼ onion (finely chopped)

Chili flakes (to taste)

For a chunky version, place ingredients in a small bowl, and mash with a fork until well-combined. For a smooth version, combine in food processor. Season with salt and pepper to taste.

Spinach and Artichoke Dip

1 batch of vegan, stretchy mozzarella-like cheese (from Chapter 5)

6 artichoke hearts, cooked, drained and chopped

½ onion finely chopped

1 cup frozen spinach

¼ cup plant-based milk (soy, almond, or oat work best here)

Salt and pepper to taste

Make the vegan, stretchy mozzarella-like cheese from Chapter 5 (you can prepare it ahead of time). Add the mozzarella to an oven-safe dish along with all the ingredients and stir. It will be lumpy but will blend well when hot. Place in a preheated oven at 200°C/395°F for twenty minutes. Stir it halfway through, and if too thick, add in extra plant-based milk. Serve with veggies or tortilla chips.

White Bean Dip

1½ cups cooked cannellini beans, drained and rinsed

2 tbsp extra-virgin olive oil

2 tbsp fresh lemon juice

1 clove garlic (crushed)

½ tsp sea salt and freshly ground black pepper to taste

¼ cup water

OPTIONAL FRESH HERBS:

2 tbsp torn fresh basil leaves

2 tsp fresh rosemary leaves

2 tbsp fresh thyme

Combine all ingredients, except water and herbs, in a food processor until smooth. Gradually add water as desired to thin the dip, and scrape down the sides of bowl as needed. Blend in herbs, and puree briefly to incorporate, if desired. Serve topped with olive oil.

MEAL IDEAS

Once you learn how to make a few simple dishes, the best part about plant-based eating is that there are so many substitute options that you can basically create ten dishes using the same recipe, just by replacing some of the vegetables. For example, you can pretty much turn anything into a stew or a soup. There are infinite combinations for good salad bowls. And any starchy vegetable could be stuffed and served. Below are some ideas.

Soups

This is a fun space to experiment because you can make soup out of many pantry items and vegetables. Lentil soup, bean soup (or chili), oat soup, onion soup, tomato soup, mushroom soup . . . you can even make good, old-fashioned, anything-in-the-fridge, clear vegetable soup which is essentially leftover veggies—like potatoes, carrots, and zucchini—chopped up and boiled in water with herbs and vermicelli noodles or orzo.

Swiss Chard and Lentil Soup

1 cup brown lentils (best if soaked for thirty minutes)
1 large potato, peeled and diced
4 cups Swiss chard leaves
4 cups water
½ cup lemon juice
1 onion, chopped
Salt and pepper to taste

In a large pot, cook onion until soft. Add lentils and potatoes, and cover with water. Bring to a boil, and simmer for twenty minutes. Once soft, add Swiss chard and juice of lemon, and simmer for another ten minutes. Add salt and pepper to taste.

Yellow Lentil Soup

   1 cup yellow/red lentils
   ¼ cup rice of choice
   6 cups water
   1 onion, chopped
   1 tbsp olive oil
   1 tbsp cumin
   Salt and pepper to taste

Soak lentils with rice for ten minutes. Meanwhile, in a pot, cook onion with olive oil until soft. Add lentils, rice, cumin, salt and pepper to pot, and cover with water. Bring to a boil, then simmer and cover. You may add more water, if needed, depending on desired soup thickness. Once lentils are cooked through, use a hand blender or food processor to give the soup a creamy texture.

Note: You can substitute the rice with 1 small potato.

Butternut Squash Soup

   ½ butternut squash
   1 sweet potato
   3 cups water (or more, depending on desired consistency)
   1 onion, diced
   1 clove garlic
   Herbs: 1 tsp rosemary, 1 tsp dried thyme
   Salt and pepper to taste

Peel and cut butternut squash and sweet potato into large cubes. Toss with olive oil, place in an oven on a baking tray, and bake for thirty minutes at 180°C/375°F, turning midway, until soft. In a large pot, cook the onion until soft. Add the roasted squash and potato into the pot with the rest of the ingredients, and add water until the veggies are covered. Bring to a boil, then simmer on low heat for twenty minutes, and use a hand blender or food processor to mix the soup. You may add more water if needed, depending on the desired soup thickness.

Clear Vegetable Noodle Soup

2 potatoes, peeled and diced
2 carrots, diced
2 zucchinis, diced
1 onion
5 cups water
¼ cup vermicelli/any small pasta
¼ cup lemon juice
1 tsp salt, and pepper to taste
Fresh coriander/cilantro (optional)

In a large pot, cook onion and carrots with olive oil. Once carrots begin to soften, add potatoes, zucchini, and water (additional water may be added, depending on the quantity of vegetables). Bring to a boil, then add vermicelli, cover, and simmer. Once vegetables are soft, add lemon juice, salt, pepper, and coriander. Cook for another five minutes, and serve warm.

❡●●

Salads

Just like soup, the fun part about a salad is that you can pretty much combine anything leftover for a great salad and add a dressing.

Salad Anything

Here are some salad bar ingredients to combine into salads

LEAFY GREENS	EVERYDAY ADD-ONS	OCCASIONAL MIX-INS	FILLING IDEAS
Lettuce (any kind)	Cucumber	Artichoke hearts	Quinoa
Kale	Tomato	Asparagus	Farro
Spinach	Baby corn	Edamame	Freekeh
Arugula	Avocado	Roasted pumpkin	Orzo
Thyme	Beetroot	Radish	Brown fusilli pasta
Collard greens	Onion	Potato/sweet	Beans
Swiss chard	Green beans	potato	Lentils
Cabbage	Mushrooms	Bell pepper	Chickpeas
Watercress	Olives	Apples	Nuts
		Figs	

Sometimes, a simple salad is the yummiest. For example, my favorite salad consists of tomato, avocado, and cucumber with lime and salt. But if you are a dressing lover, below are some of my favorites. It would be best to use a hand blender to bind the ingredients for an extra creamy consistency, but they work perfectly fine without it too.

OIL AND LEMON	LEMON VINAIGRETTE	BALSAMIC VINAIGRETTE	SWEET VINAIGRETTE
½ cup olive oil	½ cup olive oil	½ cup olive oil	½ cup olive oil
½ cup lemon juice	¼ cup apple cider	½ cup balsamic	2 tbsp any vinegar
1 tsp Dijon	vinegar	vinegar	1 tbsp maple
mustard	2 tbsp Dijon	2 tsp Dijon	syrup
1 tsp salt	mustard	mustard	1 tbsp Dijon
	4 tbsp lemon juice	1 clove garlic,	mustard
	1 clove garlic,	minced	1 clove garlic,
	minced	1 tsp salt	minced
	1 tsp salt		¼ tsp salt, to taste

Warm dishes with rice

I love warm, hearty dishes and, growing up in the Middle East, this was how we had most of our meals. My favorite thing about these dishes is that once you get used to making them, it is easy to experiment with whatever seasonal vegetables are available around you, using these simple methods.

Stew Anything

When I learned how to make stew, my meal options became endless. Stew usually consists of ingredients that have been slow-cooked in liquid and makes for a great meal served with rice. I'm going to share a recipe of green beans with tomato sauce, but this works with a lot of other vegetables too.

- 2 cups green beans (variations could be choice of: peas, okra, eggplants, zucchini)
- 2 medium-sized tomatoes, peeled and diced (or a jar of chopped tomatoes)
- 1 tbsp tomato paste
- 1 onion, finely chopped
- 1 tsp olive oil
- 1 clove garlic
- 1 cup water (more if needed)
- ¼ cup fresh coriander/cilantro
- Spices: 1 tsp cumin, 1 tsp cinnamon, 1 tsp salt, black pepper to taste

In a pot or a deep pan, heat the oil over medium heat, and sauté the finely chopped onions, garlic, coriander/cilantro, spices, and green beans (or any other veggies). Once the vegetables begin to soften, add the tomato sauce and paste, as well as some water. Add enough water so the vegetables are well covered. Bring to a boil, then simmer on low heat for twenty to thirty minutes until the sauce thickens. Add spices and herbs, and serve over rice.

Curry Anything

If you find curry paste (a little jar with curry spices), then most of the work to get the curry spices right is done for you. All you need would be:

Veggies/legumes of choice: I use potatoes, sweet potatoes, pumpkin, chickpeas, and snow peas

1 onion, diced

1 can coconut milk for cooking

2–3 tsp yellow curry paste (depending on desired intensity)

In a large pot, cook onion and add in veggies. Sauté until softened. Add coconut milk and curry paste, and allow for curry to thicken on low heat and for the flavors to settle. Serve over rice.

Spinach with Rice

6 cups spinach leaves or 1 bag frozen spinach leaves

½ cup water

1 onion

½ lemon, juiced

1 tsp salt, pepper to taste

Cook onions in a pan until soft. Add spinach on low heat and just enough water to barely cover the spinach. Once spinach is wilted, add lemon juice and salt and pepper to taste. Serve warm over rice.

Mushroom Stroganoff (or a Creamy Mushroom Sauce for Pasta)

1 cup fresh mushrooms sliced

1 onion diced

1 tbsp soy sauce

¾ cup water

¾ cup plant-based cooking cream or ¾ cup plant-based milk + 2 tbsp
  cornstarch

½ tsp smoked paprika

Salt and black pepper to taste

2 tsp Dijon mustard (optional)

1 tbsp nutritional yeast flakes (optional)

In a large pan or skillet, sauté onions until soft. Add mushrooms, and cook
for about five minutes. Pour in water, soy sauce and the spices. I love adding
nutritional yeast and Dijon mustard too. Separately, add cornstarch to the
plant-based milk, or if you find soy or oat-based cooking cream, that could
be easier. Pour the milk/cream mixture into the pan, and cook on low-
medium heat for about ten minutes until the sauce thickens. Taste and adjust
seasonings as per your preference. You can add fresh thyme leaves and/or
parsley to taste.

◍●

Quick and easy

Jackfruit Quesadillas (with Shawarma Variation)

1 can jackfruit

1 onion (optional)

¼ pack fajita spices

3 tortilla wraps

3 tbsp vegan cheddar cheese
  (from Chapter 5), or any vegan cheese

Drain jackfruit, and sauté in a pan with onion and fajita spices for about
ten minutes. Open tortilla wraps, and spread jackfruit mix on one side and
vegan cheddar cheese on the other. Fold the wrap in half, and toast in a
toaster grill. Cut into triangles and serve with guacamole.

Variation: You can use shawarma spices on the jackfruit and serve it wrapped with garlic paste or hummus, pita bread, and French fries instead of the vegan cheese and tortilla bread.

Lemon Potatoes

    2 medium potatoes peeled and cut into wedges
    ½ cup olive oil
    ½ cup lemon juice
    2 cloves garlic, crushed
    1 tbsp rosemary
    1 tsp salt, more to taste

Place cut potatoes in an oven-safe dish, and sprinkle with crushed garlic. Cover with olive oil, lemon juice, and rosemary. Bake for forty minutes at 180°C/360°F or until fork easily pierces through the potatoes.

Sweet Potato and Mushroom Mix

This is great on its own or as a base for Mexican night. I love it in tacos or burritos with red rice and guacamole.

    2 sweet potatoes, peeled and diced
    1 cup mushrooms, diced
    2 tbsp olive oil
    1 tbsp paprika
    1 tsp salt, more to taste

After cutting the sweet potato and mushroom into small cubes, place them on an oven-safe tray lined with a baking sheet. Cover with olive oil, salt, and paprika. Bake for forty minutes at 180°C/360°F or until fork easily pierces through the potatoes.

Lentils with Rice

    1 cup brown lentils
    ⅓ cup rice of choice
    1 large onion, diced
    3 cups water, more if needed
    1 tbsp olive oil
    1 tbsp cumin
    2 tsp salt

Soak lentils for twenty minutes. In a large pot, heat oil, and cook onion until browned. Add lentils and water, and bring to a boil, then lower heat and let simmer. After five minutes, add rice, cumin, and salt. Continue cooking until both, rice and lentils, are tender and the water has been fully soaked up. Water may be added as needed until fully soaked up. Serve warm topped with soy yogurt, or cold with olive oil.

Tomato and Bulgur

    1 cup coarse bulgur
    1 large onion, finely chopped
    4 medium tomatoes, peeled and diced
    2 cups water
    1 tbsp tomato paste
    1 ½ tsp salt
    Black pepper to taste

Rinse bulgur, and soak for twenty minutes. Meanwhile, cook onion with olive oil until softened. Stir in the diced tomatoes, and sauté for five to eight minutes. Add in bulgur, and cover with water, adding in tomato paste and salt and pepper. Bring to a boil, and then simmer on medium heat. Once most of the water has been absorbed, turn to low heat and cover; let it cook for an additional ten minutes until the bulgur is tender. Serve with a side salad or with soy yogurt.

Potato Salad

2 medium potatoes, cut into cubes
1 tbsp egg-free mayonnaise (you can make your own from Chapter 5)
½ tbsp lemon juice
½ tbsp dried dill
Salt to taste

Boil, bake, or steam the potatoes. Let them cool, then add remaining ingredients. Serve as a side salad.

Chickpea "Tuna" Salad

1 can chickpeas
2 tbsp egg-free mayonnaise
2 tbsp lemon juice
¼ onion (red works best)
2 dill pickles (or 1 tbsp dried dill)
1 celery stick (optional)
3–4 small sheets of roasted seaweed (optional but helps give a "fishy" taste)

Add all the ingredients to a pot and mash with a hand blender. Serve as a sandwich or on toast.

Loaded Baked Sweet Potato

2 sweet potatoes, baked
1 can black beans or red kidney beans, drained and washed
⅓ cup sweet corn
3 cups fresh spinach
¼ red onion, finely chopped
Salt and cayenne pepper to taste
Drizzle of olive oil (for pan)

Cook onions in a pan with olive oil on low heat. Add beans, corn, and spinach, and cook for about ten minutes. Split baked potatoes in half lengthwise, and add bean mixture on top.

Vegan Mac N Cheese/Béchamel Sauce

This is a great sauce for any pasta/lasagna. You can even add tomato sauce to it to make a "pink" pasta sauce version.

1 cup cashews
1 peeled potato (small)
1 tbsp nutritional yeast
½ cup any plant-based milk (or more, based on texture)
Spices: 1 tsp nutmeg, 1 tsp white pepper, 1 tsp salt

Soak cashews for two hours. Then boil and simmer with potato until the potato is tender. Move to a food processor, and mix with milk, nutritional yeast, and spices. You may need to add more milk if the sauce is too thick. Pour over cooked pasta, and stir until well combined.

*●●

The above mini-recipes are a very small overview of the world of plant-based dishes you can make. You can also find a lot of resources online for more recipes and ideas. Happy exploring!

CHAPTER 7

EATING OUT

Beyond the green salad

At home, being vegan is as easy as anything. You buy your own groceries, so when you go to grab a snack from the fridge or when you make a meal, you don't even have to give it a second thought. The part of a vegan lifestyle that can be more challenging is dining out in groups. But don't worry; we'll discuss some tips in this chapter. You've got this!

For a while, I was worried about being "that annoying friend" whom no one wants to go out with because I would spend time discussing options with the waiter and asking them to check with the chef if a dish can be made without butter, if the soup has chicken stock, or if their bread has milk in it. Then I had the only-order-French-fries-and-a-green-side-salad phase. Eventually, I realized that being at a nonvegan restaurant didn't have to be a struggle. Your friends want you to have a good meal, so they will be patient. Restaurants want you to leave happy, so they are happy to cater to your needs. Just as no one would mind you checking if anything is cooked in peanut oil when you have a peanut allergy, a good restaurant would be happy to cater to your concerns regarding veganism too. In fact, I have met a few chefs that have said they love "a good challenge," and if they don't have something to suit your needs on their menu, they are happy to create something on the spot with whatever they have lying around the kitchen.

Eventually, I fell in love with cooking and with preparing fresh clean meals at home. When I do choose to go out, I choose vegan restaurants, where I know the food will be free of animal products and where I can support small local businesses that fight for a cause I believe in. However, there are occasions when you might have to go out to nonvegan restaurants, either for certain social events or because you have no other options (think of a tiny airport with one food kiosk and a six-hour flight ahead).

In this chapter, I will share some tips for planning a meal out, things to look out for in your dishes, and some standard menu combinations that will help you master the science of subbing.

BEFORE YOU GO

In today's day and age, being vegan isn't that uncommon. And just like most places have vegetarian options, many have vegan options too. Vegans no longer have to settle for side salads and grilled veggies when eating out. More and more restaurants and cafes are now serving a selection of delicious plant-based dishes, and some even have dedicated vegan menus. Either way, I always find it best to just do a little bit of homework before I go. Here are some things you can do.

GO THROUGH THE MENU ONLINE, AND PICK OUT ITEMS BEFORE YOU GET THERE. Honestly, these days almost every restaurant has a menu online—from the fancy sushi restaurant in the business district to the dodgy falafel food truck on the corner of the alley. When I have to go out for a social gathering, I check the menu beforehand and decide if I will be able to find something. If I know I'm just going to end up with a green salad (which is unlikely), I ask the group to change the restaurant, or if it a big event and the organizers cannot accommodate me, I make sure I have a small bite to eat before I go.

FOR FINE DINING RESTAURANTS, CALL BEFOREHAND AND LET THEM KNOW. Even if they have no vegan options, the chef of any reputable fine dining restaurant would be more than happy to prepare a nice vegan meal for you if they know beforehand. I have called restaurants many times and was surprised (and thrilled) to know that they have a separate vegan menu. I wouldn't have known that unless I'd asked.

IF IT IS A SMALL GROUP OF FRIENDS, ASK IF YOU COULD PICK THE PLACE. If they care about you having fun, they wouldn't mind. You can explain that just as you wouldn't take someone with a dairy allergy to a restaurant that only serves cheese fondue, it doesn't make sense to ask you to go to a place where you don't have good food choices. Good friends are always accommodating.

AT THE RESTAURANT

Once you get to the restaurant, be clear about what you are looking for. Explain to the waiter, so he can help you pick, and be transparent about it. At first, I used to try to avoid the word "vegan." This was before it became more common, and I figured the chef might not really get what that means or might just get irritated. That's not true at all! I have heard from both chef and waiter friends that they prefer someone being clear about their limitations so they can address them correctly and without confusion. Now, I use the word "vegan" with pride, because it also helps restaurants understand that there is demand for veganism, and it prompts them to add vegan dishes as permanent menu items. The more vocal you are about this, the more change you will drive to help create a vegan world!

Here are a few tips to consider when ordering:

CHECK FOR A VEGAN OR VEGETARIAN SECTION ON THE MENU. Most restaurants have a dedicated section, or at least a little icon, next to items that indicate that those items are vegan or vegetarian, just like they do if dishes are spicy or contain nuts. Sometimes it's a little "v," sometimes a leaf, or some other icon. Just look for the guide so you can know what they stand for.

BE NICE. When you ask, just be polite. Not everyone understands what vegan is, and that is okay. If they don't know, help them out by explaining what it means and telling them what you don't eat. By being clear and friendly, you will play a role in spreading awareness and help the next person they encounter asking for the same.

BE A MASTER SUBBER. Most menus have vegetarian options which can easily be made vegan. Just ask if the dairy products or eggs can be removed from the dish to make it vegan friendly. Sometimes, when you remove an ingredient, the dish might need something else to boost it up a notch, so what I like to do is skim through the menu, and if I see another ingredient I think would work great, I might ask for a substitution. For example, when I am ordering a veggie burrito, I ask for the cheese and sour cream to be removed and be replaced with guacamole. Saying the word "sub" or "replace" is key because then, hopefully, they don't charge you extra. Sometimes, if there are no main dishes that are easily made vegan, I look at the sides. Often, there are lots of side dishes that are vegan friendly, or can be adapted, so I order a big plate of those. Once I ordered a bunch of sides—rice pilaf, sautéed vegetables, grilled asparagus, and guacamole—and I made a killer burrito bowl at a fancy French restaurant. So hey, it works!

Hidden things to look out for

Here are a few things to keep in mind when ordering:

- Some food is cooked with butter or animal ghee. It might not say so on the menu, so it's always good to ask.
- When ordering soups, check for beef/chicken stock that could be used in the base.
- Check for mayonnaise (it has egg whites) in salad dressings and sandwiches.
- Check for milk in bread and dough. In my experience, freshly made baguettes and good quality pizza dough often don't have milk, but soft breads might.
- Check for eggs in pasta. Usually, handmade pasta has eggs, but dried/packaged pasta doesn't. Most restaurants and fast-food joints would be using dried pasta, but if you are at a fancy Italian restaurant, it's safer to double-check.

CUISINE SCIENCE

Here are some ideas for what to order, depending on the type of cuisine at the restaurant. These are based on restaurants in my area that I have frequent access to, but, of course, there are many other wonderful cuisines not mentioned below that could have plenty of vegan options.

Vegan

The beauty of vegan restaurants is that you don't have to think twice; you actually have a whole menu to choose from! I know, I know, perfection. So go ahead and feast away!

Vegetarian

Many vegetarian dishes are vegan friendly. Simply check for ones that are not milk/egg-based. Sometimes, cheese toppings, for example, can be easily removed. Just ask.

Look out for: Cheese, butter, milk, eggs, honey.

Mexican

This is my absolute favorite cuisine because guacamole is life! Most main dishes like fajitas, quesadillas, and tacos can be made with beans and rice, not to mention the classic side of tortilla chips with salsa.

Look out for: Sour cream and cheese. Make sure the beans are not made with lard, and the rice isn't made with chicken broth.

Middle Eastern

Hummus please! This is where I usually find the most options. Falafel, hummus, moutabal, pita bread, tahini, baba ghanoush, stuffed vine leaves, fattoush, pumpkin kibbeh, lentil kibbeh, tabbouleh, green beans, eggplant dishes, dandelion salad, lentil dishes, rice, and couscous are all traditionally vegan.

Look out for: Cheese and yogurt toppings.

Italian

I personally find that nothing beats a pizza loaded with veggies and no cheese. It often ends up being a crowd favorite, and when we are sharing, it's the first pizza to go. Some pizza chains are now introducing vegan-cheese as well. Other options include pasta with tomato/ marinara sauce, bruschetta, bean salad, bread sticks with olive oil and balsamic, olives, grilled artichokes, and minestrone soup.

Look out for: Eggs in pasta (though, as mentioned earlier, it is more common for restaurants to serve dried pasta, which often does not contain egg), milk in pizza or bread dough, and cheese as a topping, as its commonly sprinkled on dishes even when not mentioned on the menu.

American

Vegan American cuisine includes veggie burgers, veggie dogs, French fries, sweet potato fries, onion rings, salads, baked potato, vegetable sandwiches, and potato wedges, to name a few.

Look out for: Butter, mayonnaise, buttermilk, cheese, and eggs (eggs are sometimes present in veggie burger patties as they are used to bind the patty together).

Japanese

This includes vegetable sushi rolls (you would be surprised at how great these could be), edamame, vegetable tempura, miso soup, fried tofu, *yasai katsu* curry (vegetable-based katsu), and noodle soups.

Look out for: Egg (especially in tempura batter and in ramen), fish sauce, tobiko (the orange fish eggs on sushi), and bonito flakes (fried fish flakes).

Thai

There are many options here too, with vegetable curries, vegetable pad thai, vegetable fried rolls, lemon grass or coconut soups, and several rice-based dishes.

Look out for: Eggs (especially in rice or noodles) and fish sauce (very commonly used).

Chinese

This includes vegetable spring rolls, vegetable dumplings, vegetable soups, vegetable fried rice, vegetable noodle dishes, and bean curd.

Look out for: Eggs, fish sauce, oyster sauce.

Indian

Indian food has many great vegetarian options, but they are often cooked in animal ghee (clarified butter), so it is very important to be clear and request that they are cooked with oil or vegetable ghee instead. Try the many varieties of *dal* (lentils), including *moong dal, toor dal, chana dal, urad dal,* and *masoor dal,* as well as great legume and vegetable dishes like *bhindi* (okra), *rajma* (kidney beans), *chole* (chickpea curry), *baingan bharta* (eggplant), tofu *palak* (a replacement for *palak paneer,* which is made of cheese), and *gobi matar* (cauliflower and peas). You can also try vegetable biryani, *poha* (a breakfast dish made with flattened rice and onions), and *idli* and *sambhar* (a south Indian breakfast staple of rice, or sometimes lentils, and a vegetable lentil stew).

Look out for: Ghee, butter, cream, condensed milk, paneer (cheese).

French

This could be the most challenging as butter and cream are a base for many dishes. Ask for vegetable soups, salads, baguette bread, or ratatouille.

Look out for: Butter, cream, beef/chicken stock.

Persian

A great cuisine for wholesome stews with eggplant, beans, and lentil-based dishes. A lot of them are made with eggs or milk so you can ask for vegan versions of *mizra ghasemi, khoresht bademjan, khorak lubia,* and *baghali khoresht.* Order a side of *tahdig* (burnt rice), ash soup, or *shirazi* salad. Don't forget to check out fruit sorbets for dessert.

Look out for: Ghee, yogurt, eggs, milk.

Greek

Greek cuisine has many vegan options because Orthodox fasting is common several times a year around religious holidays, which entails abstinence from meat, dairy products, and fish (but not shellfish). You can use the word "nistisimo" to ask for food that is appropriate for fasting. Some vegan foods you will find on the menu are *briam* (cooked vegetables), *gigantes* (giant beans), *gemista* (stuffed/grilled vegetables), stuffed dolmades, *melitzanosalata* (eggplant salad/spread), *kolokithokeftedes* (similar to falafel), potatoes (fried or boiled), and olives. Street vendors might have spanakopita savory pies stuffed with spinach (make sure not to get the cheese ones).

Look out for: Yogurt (*tzaziki*), honey, and cheese.

Jamaican

This includes plantains, rice and peas, veggie or potato roti, bammy, vegetable curries, jerk vegetables, callaloo, ackee (without the saltfish), roasted breadfruit, yellow yams, and boiled dumplings.

Look out for: Butter, eggs.

Ethiopian

Vegan-friendly Ethiopian cuisine consists of *injera* (a type of flatbread), lentil, peas, beans, cabbage, and greens.

Look out for: Ghee, sour cream.

Spanish

Tapas (small sharing platters) are common in Spanish cuisine, and many of them are vegan; they include artichokes, mushrooms, carrots (*zanahorias aliñadas*), *tomate aliñado*, *berenjenas fritas* (fried eggplant—make sure you mention no honey on this one), roasted bell peppers, *espinacas con garbanzos* (spinach and chickpeas), *tombet*, and the very popular *patatas bravas* (potatoes *tapas*—make sure to check that the "bravas" sauce is not made with mayonnaise). Also look for vegetable paella, *gazpacho* (cold tomato puree), and *pisto* (similar to ratatouille). Don't forget churros when it's time for dessert (or really anytime, because it is always churros-o-clock). They are mostly made vegan, but double-check.

Look out for: Cheese, cream, egg, honey.

Armenian

This is one of my favorite cuisines with fresh, mezza-style, cold dishes such as *itch* (my all-time favorite salad with a bulgur base), *haygagan salad, djagenteghi salad* (beetroot), *imam bayildi, patatesov keufte, and vospov keufte* (potato and lentil patties), *baki keufte* (usually eaten during Lent fasting), *topik* (chickpea and potato balls), and *sarma* and *zeitov dolma* (stuffed greens like vine and cabbage leaves). As for hot dishes, try *gedzou patates* (spicy potatoes) or *mante* with spinach (but make sure to ask for no yogurt as it comes mixed in).

Look out for: Cheese, yogurt.

Brazilian

While many menus are "meat"-based, the sides are full of grains and vegetables and are so filling that you can ask for them as main courses. *Arroz e feijao* (black beans and rice) is one of the most common lunch items and a great dish that is usually served with steak or eggs and a side salad, so you can ask for the black beans, rice and salad by themselves. Just make sure to ask if any meat is put in the beans, as sometimes it is made "feijoada," with beef. But, as Brazil is known for its forests and rich biodiversity, the truly unique thing about Brazilian cuisine is the fresh fruits and vegetables that can only be found there and are simply spectacular. *Aipim frito* (yuca fries) looks like French fries and is made of cassava; this is a common side dish in almost every restaurant in Brazil. Açaí is now more easily accessible across the world; enjoy a cold, fresh blend of açaí berries with toppings of your choice. Tapioca flour is also fried and served with a filling of your choice; it is made to look like a white taco but tastes unique. Pacoca is an excellent dessert made entirely out of peanuts.

Look out for: Beef/beef stock.

CHAPTER 8

COMING OUT OF THE VEGAN CLOSET

Social interactions and explaining this to Nana

When you're the only vegan at a party and gotta bring ur own food

I had to include this chapter because it was personally a long journey for me to figure out the best way to deal with my social circles when I made the decision to go vegan. There were times when I felt alienated, left out, and constantly attacked.

One time, I wasn't invited to a good friend's birthday dinner. When I found out, I asked one of my often-blunt friends about it, and he replied, "Oh, I mentioned inviting you, but they said no one wants to deal with accommodating for vegan food."

The truth is, when you start your vegan journey and begin expressing it to your family and friends, you might face some resentment, and you will not know why. You are just trying to be healthy, you choose not to kill animals, and you want what is best for the planet; it is all very noble, yet some people will attack you for it. Somehow you are either labeled as "extreme" or "annoying," or you end up being the butt of every joke. I know it doesn't sound like it makes any sense, but it's a topic that hits people at their core. This is primarily because when you say you are doing something so "good," it comes off as if you are telling the person you are talking to that the way they are is "bad," so they become defensive. In a way, their subconscious is hearing, "Did you just imply that you are so perfect and I am a cold-hearted murderer? How dare you!"

In this chapter, I will help you navigate your way through the social and emotional aspects of this journey. A lot of what is in this chapter is inspired by the work and research of Dr. Melanie Joy, PhD, a Harvard-educated psychologist, celebrated speaker, organizational consultant, trainer, and relationship coach. She is the author of the award-winning book, *Why We Love Dogs, Eat Pigs, and Wear Cows: An Introduction to Carnism*, as well as *Strategic Action for Animals* and *Beyond Beliefs: A Guide to Improving Relationships and Communication for Vegans, Vegetarians, and Meat Eaters*. She gives guidance on improving your relationships with the people around you, and I will share the tips that helped me most. We will talk about properly communicating veganism and building communities of supporters and like-minded friends.

One disclaimer for this chapter is that I will be sharing what worked for me. I am not saying this is the most effective way or that it needs to be followed to the dot; I am just sharing my journey and all the tips that empowered me. As you go through this and find your own way, you may find other methods that work better for you, and I really do hope you find a way to share them back with the world too.

TALKING TO LOVED ONES

The first people you will be excited to talk to about your transformation will be those closest to you. Back when I started learning about the cruel animal agriculture industry and its impact on our health, I was just running to the people I care about and blurting out facts. It did not go well. In retrospect, while my intention was to share all the revelations I was having, I came off as pushy, judgmental, and slightly crazy. After all, I was telling them that something so fundamental, which they have known and been practicing all their lives, was plain wrong. When we are questioning our entire way of being, something that has been so normalized for so long, we need to enable people to make their own revelations. No one wants to be told that they are wrong. In a way, everyone is on their own journey, and it's much more effective when you equip people with facts, thoughts, and ideas to support their growth at their own pace rather than just telling them why you believe that what they are doing is "so terrible."

Think about all the times in history when a minority tried to dispel a belief and how much resistance they faced for doing that, until it eventually became widely accepted. In the early 1600s, Giordano Bruno was burnt at the stake, and later, Galileo was sentenced to house arrest for supporting the Copernican theory that the earth revolved around the

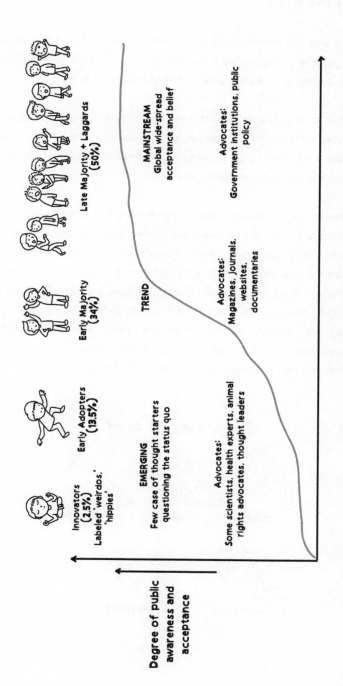

sun. We were so convinced that we were at the center of the universe that anyone who suggested otherwise was considered insane. Today, Galileo is often referred to as the father of modern science.

The earth being round, the theory of relativity, women's equality, abolishing slavery . . . all these were considered "crazy ideas" when they were suggested by an individual or a small group. Now we think it is crazy for things to have been otherwise.

Yes, there will be resistance. You cannot expect everyone to understand immediately. In fact, almost everyone I have talked to about veganism has gone through or gotten stuck at one of the five stages of grief, as enunciated by Elisabeth Kubler Ross and David Kessler, because telling someone you have chosen to do this makes them indirectly feel that you are implying that you are doing something you believe is "morally right," and they are "morally wrong." When someone is told that everything they have ever known about a certain topic is flawed, they may go through a grieving process. This is usually what happens:

The Stages of Grief

DENIAL   ANGER   BARGAINING

DEPRESSION   ACCEPTANCE

They heard what you have to say: "This is the right way to live, this is how we should treat all of earth's living creatures, it's better for your health, it's better for the environment . . . "

Denial

*Okay, this is just a trend. Are you just trying to be cool? Like that time you decided to become a guitarist or a marathon runner? I know you are gonna get over it, so I'll save that new roast beef recipe for you. *eyeroll**

What does meat have to do with the climate? Duh, my grandpa ate red meat and he's ninety-eight! Anyways, if I don't eat all the chickens, they will take over the world. There are just too many of them, and they will eat all our food.

Anger

Stop trying to control me! Ugh . . . vegans are so annoying. Who do you think you are, your holiness? Mother Teresa? Stop telling me what to do! Do you think you are better than me? Is that it? Are you stupid? I can't even take you out with me anymore because you embarrass me.

Bargaining

Okay, well, I kind of get that meat is terrible, but I will just start with meatless Mondays. I buy free range chicken; that means they had a good life before they were killed. Okay, I'm doing this, but fish doesn't count, right? If it's someone's birthday, I'm definitely eating cake.

Depression

Why is the world so cruel? How have we even gotten here? I am so upset that I have been doing this to animals and to my body! Am I even a good person? No one will understand me now. I feel so alone in this. We are all going to die anyways, so what's the point of fighting for this?

Acceptance

I didn't know before, but now I do. From today onwards, I strive to be a better version of the person I was before. This is the first day of the rest of my life. Seven tubs of hummus, please.

The reality is that you don't need everyone to understand you right away. Sure, wouldn't your life be so much easier if your partner was vegan too? If your mom didn't have to cook "special" food for you? If your friends wanted to go to the same vegan restaurants with you? But before spending all your energy fighting over this, you should know that slowly planting those seeds and leading by example is much more effective. And until they see the world the same way you do, you don't need them to be vegan too; you just need them to support you.

Remember that sometimes, trying to explain something is overshadowed by our emotions. When someone is eating meat in front of you, you may feel bad and emotionally insecure because it reminds you of slaughterhouse footage you may have watched and what that animal has gone through. It is a difficult moment for you, and when you try to express that and you end up with responses like "Vegans are so annoying" or "Don't try to control me," it can be heartbreaking. It is not easy to feel unheard and attacked, especially when you are already in a state of emotional torment. This is when it is important to try to use your emotions to help steer the conversation, but *not* to completely take over. You are less likely to be heard if you are screaming than if you are having a calm, two-way conversation.

Dr. Melanie Joy gives tips on improving relationships with the people around you. You need to know that they support you and understand you, even if they don't have the same belief system. One of my favorite tools that she presented is her letter to a nonvegan. Try sharing this letter and if they are not willing to listen, that also says a lot about your relationship with them, and that is something you should consider.

As you know, being vegan is an incredibly important part of who I am. Vegan beliefs and values are central to my life. If I feel like you don't understand this major area of my life, I feel unseen and like I can't really be my authentic self with you, like I have to keep parts of myself out of our relationship. So, I end up feeling less connected with you than I want to be.

Because I want to feel more connected with you, I want to be able to share information about veganism with you—not to try to change you or make you vegan, but so you can understand me. Basically, I need to know that you know what the world looks like through my eyes, and that's only possible if you understand enough about veganism and what it means to be vegan. By "enough," I mean sufficiently for me to feel that you really get the issue, and you get me.

I love this letter, and it worked for me particularly well when talking to people who love me and care about me, like family and close friends. But it is not always possible to talk about this so openly. Sometimes, when you are visiting your partner's grandma for a few hours in a different country, you may feel it is not worth having the conversation. Sometimes, you are invited to a dinner party at your new colleague's house, and you don't know the hosts enough to inform them that you need special food prepared. And sometimes, you go on a first date, and you want to be as delicate as possible when trying to explain this. When I first started this journey, I found it easier to just lie, which I later learned was a terrible idea. I used to say I'm allergic to dairy to make sure people are honest about whether they cooked the food with butter or not. I thought, "Hey, if Nana is offering me those tiny holiday butter cookies and she's so proud that she spent the whole night making them, I can't break her heart and tell her I refuse to try them." It was easier to say, "The doctor told me I can't have this." Or I would take it and hide it in my bag until we left. But I later learned that we need to give people more credit than that. People are not evil. They do want you to have fun when you come over to their place. They do want to be empathic toward your choices and show you that they understand you.

JUST BE HONEST. Explain what you eat and don't eat. There is nothing wrong with explaining your eating choices, just like when you have a major food allergy and are invited to someone's house and you kindly mention it when you RSVP, so you make sure you don't go into anaphylactic shock at their dinner table. The last thing someone would want is to invite you over and have you not eat, or take you out and have you only order onion rings. Save yourself the torment, but also save them the embarrassment, and just be upfront with the truth.

EXPLAIN THAT THIS IS A PERSONAL CHOICE AND AN ETHICAL BELIEF. No one argues with you if you say that you do not eat pork for religious reasons or that you want to spend Sunday morning in Church. While saying that you don't want to eat meat for health reasons will result in a long debate about the fact that we have been misled to believe it is the only way to get iron and protein, just saying it is a personal belief and that you only eat what doesn't cause harm to animals is usually easier for people to hear. Explain that your choice to go vegan is not a trendy lifestyle choice or a weight-loss diet that you can "cheat" on; it is, instead, your personal and private moral obligation. Often, I see that people tend to respect your belief systems but tend to want to debate and argue health facts.

DON'T FORGET TO PLANT SEEDS. At the end of the day, you may choose to keep this journey to yourself, and there is nothing wrong with that. But if we really do want to make a difference and steer the world toward a healthier, more sustainable, cruelty-free future, spreading a vegan message creates a ripple effect that makes a huge difference. So while it might be easier to avoid having this conversation, sometimes saying something as simple as, "Oh I don't eat animals" (instead of "I don't eat meat") really gets someone else to think. And though that will not convince them that very second and they may roll their eyes at you and walk away, you have planted a seed. And someone else, or something else, might come along and water that seed. And it may take years, but eventually, that seed may sprout, and you would have made a huge impact—not only on their lives, not only on the planet, but on the lives of animals too. Seems like a sweet deal for a few words.

RAISING CHILDREN

I get asked every day if my son is vegan. First, let me clarify that a well-planned, plant-based diet is ideal for all stages of life—including childhood. With the right planning and knowledge, a child can get everything they need. But the hardest part of raising vegan children doesn't seem to be the planning or the food; instead, it is dealing with judgmental eye rolls from the world around you. The biggest problem people seem to have is the idea that you would be "imposing your own beliefs and ethics on your children," and that the choice of whether to eat animals should be theirs. Wait a minute . . . their choice? As a parent, every single day is filled with making big and small choices on their behalf. How much screen time do I give him? Which school do I send them to? Will she get baptized? Do I buy him that new, trendy toy that every kid in his class has so he doesn't feel left out? Can she have that one cookie before dinner?

We make decisions on behalf of our children all the time, and the majority of these are either to keep them safe or to help them become the people we want them to be. The way I see it, veganism fits nicely into both categories.

KEEPING OUR CHILDREN SAFE. The moment our babies enter this world, we strive to protect them—it's pure instinct. Just as I teach my son the safety basics of crossing the road or not running with scissors, I also want to keep him safe from unbalanced eating habits, obesity, and disease. So I teach him about basic nutrition, I explain the importance of greens, and I enable him by offering a variety of plant-based foods.

HELPING THEM DEVELOP INTO THE PEOPLE WE WANT THEM TO BE.
Of course, a vegan diet for children is not only for the plant-based health benefits. Teaching kids about not eating animals means explaining the true meaning of compassion. This helps them shift the way they view the world. They learn about kindness toward all of earth's creatures and understand that every life matters.

There's a reason we take our children to pick apples but not on a tour of a slaughterhouse. We have the answers, we just need to make the connections

At the end of the day, we all want the same thing for our children. That they grow up happy. Most parents are not too particular about what career their child chooses to pursue or whom they choose to fall in love with as long as they are happy. But not harming other creatures is not so much a "choice" as it is a value. Just like teaching children to help people in need, teaching them that hitting is wrong, and teaching them to share their toys, you may want to teach the principles of veganism to your children too, especially if they are part of your core values as a parent.

And though it is a decision that is really only up to you as a parent, just like all the other parenting decisions you will make, people will judge you anyways. There is this fable I loved that my dad used to tell me when I was a kid:

An old man takes his grandson to the market to buy some potatoes. His grandson is around five years old and cannot walk long distances, so he lets him ride a donkey. Everyone starts pointing and asking, "What is wrong with this kid? He is young and healthy and he rides a donkey and lets his poor old grandpa walk next to it. How heartless!!" The grandpa feels bad and is under a lot of pressure, so they switch places. As they ride into town, everyone points and says, "Look at this old, selfish man. He lets a little kid walk while he sits like a king on that donkey. How cruel!" Confused, he gets off, and they both just walk next to the donkey. As the old man is thinking, "Good, we gave the poor donkey a break," he starts hearing people say, "Look at these two idiots. They look so tired, and they have a donkey next to them, yet they are walking." The old man and his grandson look at each other and decide that if they both get on the donkey, then no one will judge them. A minute after they both ride the donkey, they start hearing the villagers say, "How cruel are these people? They think a poor donkey can carry them both? Do they not care about how the donkey even feels?" Baffled and now worried about the donkey, the old man tells his grandson to get off quickly, and they continue walking to town, both of them carrying the donkey now!

No matter what you do, society will point fingers. You will never be perfect in everyone's eyes, so it's not worth trying or worth getting hung up over. Do what you believe is right, and there will always be a group that will not agree with it. So be it.

Raising vegan children means teaching them about healthy eating, compassion, and respect for all living beings from an early age. Are these not some of the greatest lessons we could teach our kids? Are those not values and lessons we should actually be proud of and "impose" on our children?

A few things to keep in mind when it comes to younger children specifically:

WEANING INFANTS: Speak to your health expert for an appropriate recommendation when planning the diet of young infants. During weaning, a variety of foods are to be encouraged, including vegetables, cereal foods, pulses (peas, beans, and lentils), tofu, groundnuts, seeds, and fruits. An iron-fortified infant cereal is also a great option among first foods. The cereal can be mixed with expressed breast milk or plant-based formula for a thin consistency. Nuts are great as long as your baby is not allergic to them, but make sure they are finely ground. Children under five years old should not have whole nuts because of the risk of choking. Naturally sweet fruits (such as apples or bananas) or vegetables (such as carrots, sweet potatoes, or butternut squash) can be used to sweeten foods instead of sugar. Never add artificial sweeteners, sugar, or salt to foods for infants.

QUANTITY CHECK: Plant-based diets tend to be less calorie dense, so children need to eat larger quantities to get enough energy. We know that children typically have small appetites, so achieving their daily calorie needs can be a challenge. Adding healthy oils to food, such as olive oil or cold-pressed rapeseed, is key as they add more calories to meals and encourage the production of important fatty acids, which are needed for brain development.

CALCIUM: Calcium is key for maintaining healthy bones, and approximately 45 percent of our bone mass is accrued before the age of eight years. A cup of plant-based milk that's been fortified with calcium and vitamin D is a good choice, and you may wish to include soy yogurts, plant-based spreads, and calcium-rich cereals. Almonds, calcium-set tofu, beans, and green leafy vegetables are also good sources of calcium and should be regularly included in your child's diet. Calcium recommendations vary with age, so it would be great to keep a sense check on those.

IRON: Iron is essential for the formation of red blood cells. Just like adults, children should regularly consume good sources of iron, such as beans, lentils, peas, dark green leafy vegetables (like broccoli, okra, watercress, or spring greens), whole meal bread and flour, nuts, wholegrains, and fortified cereals in their diet. Dried fruits such as apricots, prunes, and figs are also good choices. By combining an iron-rich food with a vitamin C rich one, you will help increase iron absorption; try oranges on a fortified breakfast cereal or green peppers with lentils in a vegetable casserole.

Be sure to keep yourself well informed about the key nutrients required for growth and development, and ensure that children are eating a balanced diet. You may want to seek professional guidance, where necessary.

BUILDING A COMMUNITY

Your journey does not have to be a struggle or a constant debate with people around you. There are times when you are just not up for having this conversation. Your world does not have to be about you ending up singled out at the table, where the conversation turns into a mix of "Oh no, you are biting into that cucumber. It must be feeling so much pain" types of jokes and the ever-so-trivial passing-the-sausages-from-right-under-your-nose with an "Oh, I'm sorry. Does my food bother you?"

I honestly don't think anything has been as important for my journey as finding vegan friends. Just like anything in life, you need to find people who share your belief systems because belonging to a group of like-minded individuals is simply good for the soul. Just like you would join a spiritual book club when you want to discuss divine literature, or play Sunday chess at the park to get some serious competition and tips when no one at home plays well enough, sometimes you just need to seek situations where you can feel like you belong. Having a sense of belonging is a basic human need, like the need for food and shelter. Some find belonging in neighborhood coffee mornings, some with good friends, some with family, and some on social media. Some see themselves as connected only to a couple of people and others to a whole group. Some even believe in and feel a connection to a higher power. Whatever it may be, a sense of belonging to a greater community improves your health, happiness, and drive. When you feel a connection to others, you know that all people struggle and have difficult times. All people triumph with little victories. You are no longer alone, and there is always comfort in that knowledge.

You may not have vegan friends in your immediate circles that you can discuss this transformation with, but that doesn't mean you shouldn't be seeking them. Whether it's one person or an entire group, you need to find what works best for you and actively look for it. I originally struggled with finding a community to belong to, so I actively created one. I launched the Dubai Vegan Community as a social media page to seek friends, and within just the first month, a thousand people joined it. It was a beautiful expression of just how many people needed this sense of belonging. The group kept growing, and we started meeting in person. It helped many people to find belonging in a new family, form close, intimate friendships, and even meet partners for small, vegan business ventures.

It might not always be easy and comfortable trying to make new, like-minded friends; it requires active effort and practice.

FIND THE CROWDS FIRST, THEN THE RELATIONSHIPS WILL FOLLOW.
Attending events or joining animal shelter and beach cleanup volunteer groups is a great way to find compassionate individuals who care about their communities and the planet. Some people tell me, "Yes, but we don't want to be with a big group, we just want to find a friend." Even though it might be overwhelming being alone in a big group when you get there, it is a first step to eventually finding people you click with and can form close bonds with from within that group. It may not happen from day one, but it's a great first step to forming new friendships.

FIND COURAGE TO MAKE THE FIRST MOVE. Join or start a small social media group on apps like Meetup or Facebook and call for people to come together by organizing a night out or hosting a vegan potluck dinner. Once you put yourself out there, you will be surprised to discover how many people are looking for the same type of relationship. Even if one person ends up coming, which is unlikely, that's still a great victory— finding one new friend to discuss this journey with.

FIND WAYS YOU ARE SIMILAR, NOT WAYS YOU ARE DIFFERENT. One of my favorite groups to hang out with is a group of three vegan friends. The four of us met initially through small talk at different community events, and we eventually found ourselves always drawn to sit together. We love art, we have the same sense of humor, and we spend dinners discussing famous animal rights activist crushes. Though we grew up on different continents, our ages basically cover three decades, and we are at very different life stages when it comes to family and career, we always focus on what brings us together. It is a beautiful experience to become such good friends with people who are very different. You learn a lot from each other, you grow together, and you lift each other up.

YOU'VE GOT THIS!

It is not easy. We live in a world that offends our deepest values every day. We live in awareness of the atrocities that are happening to animals, public health and the environment, and while we are concerned, people think there is something wrong with us. Yes, it can be stressful. You might be at dinner tables and get asked the most random, often ridiculous questions. In the next chapter, we will tackle some of the key comments you might hear, and I will try to empower you with possible logical answers that could help relieve some of the tension such discussions bring.

At the end of the day, whether this journey ends up being smooth sailing or tough on some of your relationships, you need to be proud of yourself. You are trying to transform your health and stand up for what you believe is right. It takes courage, compassion, and commitment to do this every day. You are part of a social justice movement that will change the world.

CHAPTER 9

RESPONDING TO CRITICISM

Answers to everyday dinner table comments against veganism

The Hardest Part of Being Vegan

⊠ EATING OUT AT RESTAURANTS

⊞ EATING AT A FRIEND'S HOUSE

▨ GET ENOUGH VITAMINS

Ⓦ FINDING VEGAN PRODUCTS

☐ DEALING WITH RIDICULOUS COMMENTS

An often-circulated online joke is that the hardest part about going vegan is dealing with ridiculous comments.

Yes, these comments warrant their own chapter because learning how to deal with them is essential to staying sane. So for the sake of your mental health, in this chapter, we will review what you can expect—arguments that will make you roll your eyes—and share possible answers that will help you remain calm in a conversation.

To start off, you might often feel that these statements are more like attacks, especially from people who are not very close to you and have not discussed their choices with you.

Why? Because a lot of people just don't like being around vegans.

Though it's natural for people to disagree, the passionate rage in arguments, the outbursts of sarcasm, and the attacks you might face at a dinner table seem to defy rational sense. In fact, research has shown that vegans often stir up the same degree of loathing as drug addicts. Given that most of us would probably like to be healthier and would like to see less suffering in the world, why is there such resentment toward those who do something about it? Psychologists are now starting to understand why, and it's becoming clear that the widespread resentment is not driven by our conscious awareness but instead goes down to deep-rooted psychological biases.

"Cognitive dissonance" occurs when a person holds two incompatible views and acts on one of them. If you are eating fish and chips right in front of your beloved goldfish swimming in her aquarium or if you are scrolling through adorable pictures of #rabbitsofinstagram when Grandma calls up and says she's just made your favorite rabbit stew, you are likely to encounter "cognitive dissonance." In this case, your affection for animals might start to clash with the idea that it's normal to eat them. The resulting tension in the mind can make us feel stressed and irritated. But instead of resolving it by changing our beliefs or behavior, it's quite normal to, without realizing it, ignore these feelings and blame them on something else entirely. Some psychologists call this the "meat paradox."

Dr. Hank Rothgerber, a social psychologist at Bellarmine University, Kentucky, suggests that we have developed a number of strategies which allow us to avoid facing up to the meat paradox. These include pretending that meat has no link to animals (we call it beef, not cow, to forget where it came from), imagining that we eat less of it than we actually do (saying, "Oh I just have it once a week,"), ignoring how it's produced, and insisting that we only eat meat which is "humanely" farmed. We do all this while being helped by the cartoons of happy farm animals that we're exposed to from early childhood on TV commercials and milk bottles.

These strategies work. But unfortunately, they become interrupted by the presence of vegans. When a vegan turns up at a dinner party, other guests suddenly feel pushed out of their comfortable "mainstream diet"/ the "norm" category and into the unsettling "meat-eating" category. By their mere existence, without having to say a word, vegans force people to confront their cognitive dissonance. And this makes people angry.

The reason I share all this is because if you ever feel attacked, it is important to understand where people are coming from. This is not a personal attack toward you. You are living your best life and making the world a better place; hats off to that. The problem is much more deep-rooted in human psychology and a "norm" that has been created over the years. It is therefore very important to remain calm, understand where the person is coming from, and know that this choice you are making is not necessarily easy for others to digest immediately.

Below are some of the comments and arguments I hear most often. With friends and family, I tackle these by having honest, open conversations about my choice and sharing the "vegan letter" (in Chapter 8). However, at parties and work events, when a conversation is casual, I try to give short, calm, and logical answers while trying to effectively plant seeds that people can take away and hopefully think about when they go home afterwards.

"Well, we need animal products to survive."

That is simply not true. The many plant-based thought leaders in history and the many vegans today are all proof that we do not really need to eat animal products for survival purposes in this day and age. People eat beef, chicken, fish, milk, cheese, and eggs because they enjoy the taste. Double stuffed pepperoni pizza, a chocolate glazed Boston Cream donut, and a Grande cow-milk Iced Latte with extra whipped cream are not in any way "survival foods." We can survive without all these foods (though in case we really crave them, they all have a plant-based version); they are not "essential for our existence." In fact, it seems that animal products, and the way we are manufacturing them today, with antibiotics and hormones and terrible living conditions for the animals, are not only not needed for survival, but have become detrimental to our health. (Refer to Chapter 2 and the references at the end of this book for more details on the impact of animal products on our health.)

"But we are omnivores, look at my canines."/"We can digest meat so we are made to eat it."

We also tackled this in Chapter 2, showing that biologically we are actually similar to herbivores (do refer to the chart there for support). Our teeth are in no way carnivorous and those two pointy teeth are commonplace in various species of herbivores such as rhinos, hippos, and gorillas. If someone really does believe that our small apple-crunchers (which cannot bite through a pillow, let alone flesh and blood) and our jaws that move sideways to grind plants instead of opening wide to bite into an animal, are in any way carnivorous, then the answer is: just because we have a body part that is capable of doing something, it doesn't mean we should do it. We can make a fist, but this doesn't mean we should go around punching people.

If you put how we are built aside, sure, humans *can* eat and digest animal products, but that doesn't automatically mean we should. Technically, we can also eat paper, Play-Doh, chalk, cling film, dirt, and clay. We "can" also eat artificial food coloring and additives. We "can" digest highly processed meats that give us a higher risk of colon cancer, type 2 diabetes, and heart disease. We even once ate a raw beef ravioli product that was later recalled from the market due to possible *E. coli* contamination.

Besides, if humans did have carnivorous instincts, we would not be repulsed by slaughterhouse footage. We would stop on the highway to pick up roadkill, and we would salivate whenever we saw another animal. An instinct is an innate pattern of behavior that is not the result of learning, choosing, or experiencing something. It is programmed into the genetic code of everyone in that species, and it is something that every single member of the species does naturally; it is beyond control. Examples of human instinct include breathing without even thinking about it, laughing while getting tickled, shivering when cold, and flinching if something catches you by surprise. Eating meat or drinking milk are not human "instincts." If you give a baby a bunny and a grape, he will not think to eat the bunny but will probably put the grape in his mouth. That is how we instinctively see food as modern humans.

Simply put, vegans are living proof that humans can live long, healthy lives without eating any animal products whatsoever, and they have the same biological makeup (teeth, digestive enzymes, and so on) of any nonvegan person; thus it is unnecessary to harm animals or expose our bodies to their flesh (the definition of meat) when there are alternatives.

"But I only eat halal/humanely slaughtered animals/ organic meat."

Many people will argue that eating meat is part of nature, but their conscience is clear because their meat suffered less. This so-called humane meat shows us that we have a desire to do the right thing or treat other animals with kindness, but we also do not want to face the bigger issue and reflect on whether we should be eating them in the first place.

The term "humane slaughter" is an oxymoron; it makes as much sense to say it as it does to say "humane slavery" or "humane murder." Just ask the person who is saying this to think about whether there is a nice way to kill someone who doesn't want to die. Would they be happy to be killed for no good reason if they were promised that the process will be painless or that they would be killed with "respect and honor"? Would that make any difference in their choice to die? Given that animals want to live and value their lives as we value ours, there is just no nice way to kill them. In any case, anyone looking at the methods used today in animal agriculture, such as gas chambers or bolt guns, can see for themselves that no matter what "label" is put on it, it is not "humane."

As for the focus on organically raised animals, "organic" also totally ignores the ethical issues, as that animal will still be killed eventually, which, as I've highlighted, is simply unnecessary as we can live healthier lives without meat. Organic meat also does not help reduce the problems of growing levels of obesity, diabetes, and cancers linked to meat consumption.

"How are eggs not vegan? I just want to eat an egg that wasn't even fertilized, so technically no chicks are dying."

"Technically," they are dying. A common misconception is that chickens are just naturally "giving" eggs. Modern egg hens have been intensively bred to lay between 250 and 300 eggs a year, while in the wild, chickens, like all birds, lay around 10–15 eggs per year, only during breeding season or just enough to assure the survival of their genes. This industry, that forces the production of massive quantities of eggs, also kills millions of newborn male baby chicks every single day. After all, there is no use for male chicks. They will never lay eggs and are not the breed sold for meat (meat chicken breeds have been genetically manipulated to grow much more breast muscle and flesh) and therefore, it is a common worldwide practice to toss them out as they are considered worthless to the egg industry.

Making Sense of Eggs

	CAGE	BARN LAID	CERTIFIED FREE RANGE	CERTIFIED ORGANIC
ARE HENS CONFINED IN CAGES?	YES	NO	NO	NO
ARE HENS PROVIDED WITH A NEST/PERCH?	NO	YES	YES	YES
DO HENS HAVE SPACE TO FLAP THEIR WINGS/EXERCISE?	NO	YES (Restricted)	YES	YES
DO HENS HAVE ACCES TO AN OUTDOOR RANGE?	NO	NO	YES	YES
ARE HENS 'DEBEAKED'?	YES	YES	MAYBE (DEPENDS ON CERTIFICATION BODY)	NO
ARE MALE CHICKS KILLED AT BIRTH?	YES	YES	YES	YES
ARE HENS SENT TO SLAUGHTER FROM 18 MONTHS OLD?	YES	YES	YES	YES

"Plants have feelings too, you know; you are murdering this lettuce right now."

This is really the most ridiculous argument, but ironically the one I get most. It is absurd because the vast majority of people on this planet know that it is insane to compare picking an apple or even cutting a plant to, let's say, cutting a puppy. It is actually a trivialization of animal suffering to compare the slaughter of any animal to lettuce, for example, and on some level, everyone already knows that.

I have also heard about yeast being "living bacteria." Again, it is a huge trivialization of sentient animal life to compare animals to non-sentient life forms such as bacteria. When someone makes such an argument, they essentially compare animal life (and indeed human life, as humans are animals biologically) to a slice of bread.

But the thing is, if anyone arguing with you actually does think that harming a plant is comparable to harming animals, then it makes absolute sense to go vegan always, because it actually requires far fewer plants to feed a vegan than it does to feed a nonvegan (about ten times fewer), due to the large amount of crops used to raise livestock. Veganism actually minimizes land use, crop use, and water use, and lowers the amount of deforestation, as rainforests are being constantly cleared for animal agriculture.

"But you can't get enough protein."

This is a grandma or gym enthusiast's favorite. We tackled this in detail in Chapter 2, and the fact that a well-balanced, plant-based diet will be more than adequate for protein. Given that no one they know has ever died from protein deficiency, but several—vegan or not—have suffered from heart disease or diabetes, maybe protein should not be the biggest nutritional concern. Besides, the strongest land animals on the planet (like gorillas, rhinos, elephants, giraffes, and hippos) are all predominantly herbivores, fueling their superior muscle strength with a diet of plants.

"Omg, you ate deep-fried falafel and used a plastic fork," or "Omg, you stepped on an ant, you self-hating, hypocritical, earth-hurting murderer."

The funny thing about discussing this lifestyle with anyone is that many people immediately think you are claiming to be a better person than them. So they wait for a chance to jump in and say, "Ah, I caught you; you are a hypocrite." But you never claimed to be better, and you definitely didn't claim to be a perfect saint. All you are trying to do is try your best, eat as well as possible, and live as peacefully as possible.

I was jogging once, and a workout buddy pointed out, "Oh my God. I think you just stepped on an ant. You claim to be vegan, but you are a hypocrite." This is just silly because to compare actively and willingly killing for food (when you have ample other options that are also better for you and for the planet) to accidentally causing harm is like saying, "Oh, I tripped and pushed this kid by mistake. Eh, might as well just beat him up then."

The way I usually answer this is, "I am not perfect nor ever claim to be, but every day I am striving to be a better version of the person I was the day before. Sure, I might sometimes, either by accident or because I had no other choice, end up doing something I wouldn't have wanted to, but I learn and grow every day, and I am just trying my best."

"Animals eat other animals."

While it is true, of course, that animals do eat other animals all the time in nature, we don't base our own ethics and decisions solely on the action of animals. Otherwise, we would have been able to justify sexually attacking other people without their consent (hey, animals do it), urinating on someone's front lawn (dogs do it), smothering babies to death (lions do it), vomiting on people's food (flies do it), and so on. We only seem to be interested in justifying human behavior with one thing animals do, but not the others.

"Being vegan is expensive."

Veganism can be as expensive or inexpensive as you want it to be. Sure, some specific meat and cheese substitute brands are new to the market and might be expensive and chopped up and prepackaged kale or a store-bought quinoa salad might be overpriced, but the reality is that a plant-based diet can be the least expensive one on the planet. Just think about the staple foods of most of the developing countries in the world: rice, beans, lentils, potatoes, and bread. Actually, for much of the world, meat is a luxury item.

Perhaps meat has become so commoditized that it has become "cheap" enough to buy a burger for a dollar. But think about the quality of that meat. One dollar with bread, cheese, a tomato, sauce, kitchen equipment, and labor factored in. Do you really think a piece of meat should cost so little?

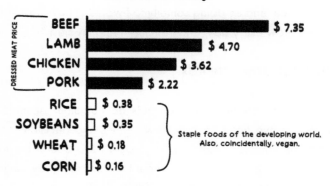

"Veganism is a first world luxury"
No, not really

DRESSED MEAT PRICE		
BEEF		$ 7.35
LAMB		$ 4.70
CHICKEN		$ 3.62
PORK		$ 2.22
RICE		$ 0.38
SOYBEANS		$ 0.35
WHEAT		$ 0.18
CORN		$ 0.16

Staple foods of the developing world. Also, coincidentally, vegan.

Commodity prices, per kilogram

"You ate meat for thirty years, now you are going to pretend you are bothered."

I heard this often from my extended family early on when I began walking away from dinner tables that had no vegan options. The conversations we discussed in Chapter 8 are essential here. It is very important to be open and honest about the feelings that seeing animal products stir up. Whether it is because you really care about your body and well-being and you genuinely do not want chicken broth in your soup, or because you have been exposed to the atrocities the animals go through in the slaughter process, it is your right to be "bothered" about having animal products in your food or even around the table. There is nothing wrong with not wanting to "just pick off" the cheese from the salad, with wanting your food to be cooked with oil instead of butter, or with not wanting to be at a dinner table with a whole, roasted, stuffed turkey in the middle of it.

Dr. Melanie Joy talks about a very interesting concept of secondary-traumatic stress disorder, which is like PTSD, except that it comes from witnessing violence, rather than from being a direct victim. When you see slaughterhouse footage and later see an animal product on the dinner table, it is normal for those images to come flashing back, and you actually feel anxious and upset about the animal suffering embedded in the food in front of you. This is especially pervasive among animal rights activists due to the extent of animal cruelty they witness. Do not let anyone make you feel that it is wrong that you didn't feel this way before but do now. You are entitled to develop new outlooks to the world; this is what personal growth looks like. You are evolving and your consciousness is shifting. Embrace it and love every second of it.

"The animal is already dead."

It's true that buying an animal product from a supermarket means that that specific animal wouldn't really care, as it is already dead. But funding that industry is what got it killed in the first place, and buying that product means funding the making of another one just like it to replace the one on the shelf. This is the reality of a supply and demand economy.

Choose the role you want to play and stand up for its values, regardless of the realities of the harsh world around us. If you saw a plastic bag in the ocean, you wouldn't say, "Ah, the ocean is already dirty, so I might as well throw my trash in too."

"It is a personal choice. Stop trying to force your beliefs on me."

Depending on who is saying this, you could answer in different ways.

If it is someone close to you that you care about, focus on the positive impact of a plant-based diet, and explain that you are not trying to force your beliefs but you are instead just trying to share the knowledge that you recently came across. Talk about the amazing health impacts they can reap, and emphasize that it is only because you care about them and their health that you care to share your beliefs.

If it is someone you don't know very well, chances are you never tried to "force your beliefs" but were simply answering their questions to begin with, and you can merely explain that. If they keep insisting that it is their "choice," you can explain that supporting animal agriculture cannot be a personal choice because there is someone else in the equation: the animal. A favorite song, a haircut, a vacation destination . . . those are personal choices. Enslaving, oppressing, and marketing a potential carcinogen as a "muscle builder" are not. Nonhuman animals in no way consent to the harms enacted upon them, and thus have no "choice."

"There are other, more important issues going on in this world."

I was talking to a close friend once about the egg industry and how doctors basically recommend that we consume no more than 300 milligrams (mg) of dietary cholesterol per day, while just having two eggs for breakfast already exceeds that. Then I went on to say that anyways the egg industry is one of the cruelest out there because all the male baby chicks are automatically ground or crushed as they cannot become egg-laying hens. I expected that she would be touched by this appalling fact, but instead, she looked at me and screamed, "There are bigger issues in the world right now. There are children dying in a war in Syria and you care about baby chicks?"

At first, I was really upset. She made me question my moral judgment, and I thought, "Wow, was I described as insensitive?" Then I realized that standing for one cause does not mean you negate or care less about another! We unfortunately live on a planet with war, genocide, murder, and assault, but caring for anything else doesn't negate our feelings toward those.

It takes nothing away from a human to be kind to an animal.

—JOAQUIN PHOENIX

Besides, it is not a cause that is far off from caring for human "issues." Heart disease is the number-one cause of death today. There is also a proven direct link between supporting the animal agriculture industry and violence toward humans. A joint study by the University of Windsor and Michigan State University concludes that when a slaughterhouse is opened in a particular area, rates of violent crime, robbery, and rape in that area show a significant increase as a direct cause of slaughterhouse employment. As Leo Tolstoy said, "As long as there are slaughterhouses, there will be battlefields."

CHAPTER 10

A SPIRITUAL REBIRTH

The accidental consequence of eating more mindfully

A man can
live and be
healthy without
killing animals
for food.
Therefore, if
he eats meat,
he participates
in taking life
merely for
the sake of
his appetite.

—LEO TOLSTOY

BEYOND A PHYSICAL TRANSFORMATION

You may have heard of many stories of transformations attributed to a plant-based diet such as people fully moving to it and curing heart disease, losing weight, reversing arthritis and type 2 diabetes, or even curing cancer. If you haven't, I can tell you they are out there. I myself have seen my body transform. I lost a lot of the unhealthy weight I was carrying from years of cheeseburgers and pizza; I had had anemia since childhood, which I finally recovered from; I got rid of my acne, and my skin was glowing; and my energy levels went through the roof. I, a lifelong couch potato, started exercising two hours a day while taking care of a toddler, managing my own business, and excelling at my full-time corporate job.

But this isn't the intention of this chapter.

At the end of the day, you don't need a thousand inspiring success stories or a nutrition scientist to tell you that if you naturally start eating more greens and less processed food you will start to feel better. That is what a plant-based diet usually results in. Let's take weight loss, for example. Losing weight, in general, is a very simple science of calories. A calorie is a unit that measures energy and is used to measure the energy content of foods and beverages. To lose weight, you need to eat fewer calories than your body burns each day. No crazy, crash fad diets are as effective (or as sane) as just realizing that our body needs to be fed well, with enough calories but not too many, to stay in shape. Science simply tells us that one pound of fat is equal to 3,500 calories. For example, to lose a pound of fat in a week, you need to be at a 3,500 caloric deficit, which means that you need to consume 3,500 calories less than your body needs that week. What a plant-based diet does is very simple—it loads you up with healthy food, making it much easier for you to stay in your calorie range as you eat nutritious foods. Plant-based foods help to really fill you up for naturally less calories, so you feel strong, energized, and satiated while empty calorie foods don't provide your body with the nutrients you need to live an active, fit life. And when you eat junk food, you're likely to get hungry more often and overeat as a result.

So naturally, you will hear many stories of people who shifted their eating habits to a plant-based diet and lost a lot of unwanted weight. They feel great, they look great, their bodies run on nutritiously dense foods, and their energy levels are at their best. Some people also choose a vegan lifestyle only for ethical reasons and disregard the healthy eating part. You can be vegan and just live on Oreos, deep-fried foods, and chips.

What I really didn't expect along this journey, however, and what has been my absolute favorite part of it, is the spiritual transformation that comes with eating more mindfully.

AN AWAKENING

I was not raised by hippy parents selling crystals and reading palms in tie-dye hemp robes at a local farmer's market, as the stereotype often goes. My extended family was relatively religious and conservative, and I grew up with Sunday family barbecues and cream cheese sandwiches in my lunchbox every day. So I never expected that my food choices would be so intrinsic to my spiritual growth. But somehow, they were.

After a while of realizing that my body was no longer carrying the stress and hormones of other once-living beings, I remember experiencing a kind of shift in consciousness. I felt lighter, as though a weight I'd been carrying my whole life had been lifted off my shoulders. Sure, I have always liked animals, though I hadn't considered myself an "animal lover" in the past, but I suddenly found myself full of compassion, empathy, and reverence for all other living beings, including other humans. It was as if my conscience was truly clear for the first time ever. A clean slate.

My Personal Journey Timeline

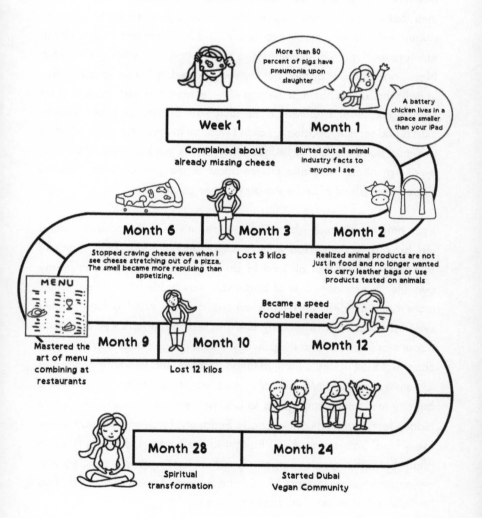

I also felt a shift in the way I viewed the world. Perhaps it was because this idea challenged what I had always known as "normal" that I started questioning other cultural ideologies I'd always had. Was there anything else that I just grew up assuming was true without questioning it? It was then that I realized how a lot of the thought patterns I had built were rigged with bias and media brainwash. Suddenly, the term "inspirational entrepreneur" no longer referred to a man in a suit walking down the New York financial district, but instead referred to Simon, a taxi driver in Bali who left his home at the age of seventeen and went door to door cleaning dishes at restaurants till he could save up enough to buy a car to start a taxi service. Suddenly, I didn't want all my medical advice from a pre-med student at an Ivy League university as much as I wanted it from an energy healer who talked to me about aligning my chakras while we sipped on a blend of herbs she grew in her garden.

I not only developed a beautiful new sensitivity to the people around me, but also to the person within me. The idea of a world full of cruelty and terror meant that all I could do to balance it out was to fill my own life with random acts of kindness. I was suddenly more generous, more open-minded, and more curious to understand different belief systems. I explored astronomy and tracked the moon's cycles. I read about manifestation and the power we hold in our thoughts to drive true change. I took up my own meditation practice and felt more connected to nature than ever. My idea of a great vacation was no longer seeing big city monuments and going to wild parties, but escaping to explore hidden forests and trek ancient trails. Suddenly, I was on a mission where everything, from the clothes I bought to the career I led, had to be in alignment with a greater purpose . . . where just "existing" in society was no longer enough. Instead, I had to be a force of positive energy; I had to make a difference; I had to change the world.

Several people I've spoken to have described similar experiences, and many in the vegan community consider themselves to be spiritual. At first,

I wondered why the connection between veganism and spiritual growth seemed to be so strong, but I soon realized the following truths:

We are what we eat

The phrase, "You are what you eat," originally came into the English language from Anthelme Brillat-Savarin, in *Physiologie du Goût, ou Méditations de Gastronomie Transcendante, 1826*, who said, "Dis-moi ce que tu manges, je te dirai ce que tu es." (Tell me what you eat, and I will tell you what you are.) Brillat-Savarin did not mean for that to be taken literally. He was stating that the food one eats has a bearing on one's state of mind and is indicative of an individual's personality, temperament, and his attitude toward others and the world.

When we eat animal products, many suggest that we invite in the negative vibrations of an animal that suffered for our food or that died a terrifying death. That vibrational energy, carrying turmoil, torment, and pain, is far from positive, and their suffering literally becomes a part of us.

Others say that natural stress hormones, as well as the added hormones in meat, are taken in by our bodies. Since we use the food that we eat and its nutrients to build new cells, our cells are nourished by it, and that food, with all that it is carrying, literally becomes us. We can therefore choose what we want our bodies to be made of and, in turn, what energy we carry around inside us.

Perhaps this explains the feeling of "lightness" experienced by several new vegans. Many people begin to feel, as they transition, that eating plant-based food nourishes their mind, body, and spirit, and naturally raises their vibrations. Though I didn't realize this at first, with time, I personally began to feel more at peace knowing that my energy was clear of the suffering of other sentient beings.

Veganism and religion

Religion, the cultural manifestation of any spiritual ideology, has long promoted a connection between compassion to animals and spirituality. I have met people practicing different religions who have spoken about their spiritual "enlightenment" when they took a decision to become vegan and how it brought them closer to their core beliefs and their devoutness.

The core tenets of virtually all religions dictate treating all living and sentient beings with kindness. All the major religions have a rule along the lines of "Treat others as you would like to be treated" and "Thou shalt not kill." Some argue that this does not apply to animals, as religious narratives sometimes include sacrificing an animal. They sometimes try to justify this by claiming that animals don't have souls, or that they are less important than humans, or that God put them here for us to eat. But in all these stories, the animal was sacrificed out of a "necessity," and killing them for pleasure's sake only would have been a sin. To those who believe a beef burger is a necessity in the twenty-first century, I usually answer:

In a world where research tells us a plant-based diet is the best way to thrive, where the standard American diet with processed animal products is making us all ill, where thanks to modern agriculture techniques we have access to all kinds of fruits and vegetables at our doorstep across seasons, where we are not in the middle of an Ice Age or a desert or a famine, where we are smart and competent enough as a civilization to come up with delicious meat and dairy substitutes that taste almost exactly the same, why is killing still considered a "necessity"?

The more ancient Eastern religions, such as Hinduism, Buddhism, and Jainism also believe in the virtue of "ahimsa," roughly translated as "nonharming," and followers of these religions are encouraged or even required to practice vegetarianism. Ahimsa applies to all creatures, as they are all believed to have divine spiritual energy. Since we all share this energy, hurting others means hurting ourselves. In other words, everything is connected—the way we treat animals has serious repercussions for our society.

We are all connected

There is a thread that joins us all together . . . plants, people, animals, and all sentient life. When we tug at that thread, we find that everything is connected. What we do to another, we ultimately do to ourselves.

There are many examples of the repercussions of our choices. Slaughterhouse workers often develop PTSD and become violent toward members of their communities. Animal agriculture is one of the leading drivers of climate change which is causing extreme weather, such as droughts, and floods, and destroying villages, homes, and essential crops. The consumption of animal products is linked to chronic diseases like heart disease, type 2 diabetes, cancer, and hypertension. And a billion people are going hungry, partly because we feed so much of the crop that we grow to farmed animals.

As a civilization, we have been unkind to the planet around us and to its resources (including its animals), and the consequences have been dire. These choices are connected, like dominos, and when we knock over a piece, it knocks another until it is out of our control. In the past fifty years, unsanitary factory-farm sheds crowded with thousands of chickens, pigs, or cows and wet markets selling the flesh of wild animals, have been breeding grounds for new zoonotic pathogens. COVID-19 in 2020, the Ebola outbreak in 2014, MERS in 2012, swine flu in 2009, SARS in 2002, H5N1 bird flu in 1997, and Creutzfeldt-Jakob disease (or "mad cow" disease) in 1995 are all linked to meat production and consumption. When we stress and injure animals, when we cage sick

A human being is a part
of the whole, called by us
"Universe," a part limited
in time and space.
He experiences himself,
his thoughts and feelings
as something separated
from the rest, a kind
of optical delusion of
his consciousness.
This delusion is a kind of
prison for us, restricting
us to our personal desires
and to affection for a few
persons nearest to us.
Our task must be to free
ourselves from this prison
by widening our circle of
compassion to embrace all
living creatures and the whole
of nature in its beauty.

—ALBERT EINSTEIN (1879-1955)

animals in public areas, when we simply abuse our power and nature's resources, it is only a matter of time before the thread that is connecting us catches fire.

I have met several people who became vegan not for health reasons, but because they faced an immense moral consideration on a journey of spiritual awakening and personal growth. As they had a shift in consciousness, they began asking questions such as:

Do I really want to be a part of that destruction?

What role do I want to play on this planet? What contribution to humanity will I offer?

Why continue to take part in the killing and torture of other beings when I don't have to?

Why approve of an eating habit that is contributing to the destruction of the earth?

Why contribute to an industry that causes severe emotional pain and mental suffering to other human beings who are expected to do the "dirty work" for me behind slaughterhouse doors?

Because they felt connected to the karmic powers of the universe, the choice to remove animal foods from their diet became obvious and automatic.

BE IN ALIGNMENT WITH YOUR VALUES

When our beliefs and actions are not aligned, it can be distressing. In our hearts, we all know that hurting other creatures is wrong and that all life should be respected. Practicing veganism simply means rejecting the exploitation of other sentient beings and truly aligning our actions with our beliefs. It is a personal honoring of the interconnectivity of the universe.

We are blessed to live in a world where we can enjoy delicious and abundant food without harming or exploiting animals. A lifestyle which causes minimal harm to other life forms ultimately benefits everyone and everything else on the planet, because everything is connected. Spiritually, we understand that everything is made of energy. In fact, these days, even science confirms it. Everything consists of a vibration, and without vibrational energy, nothing would exist at all. The physical, emotional, mental, and spiritual choices we make in life dictate and alter our energetic vibration.

With time, it became clear to me that a compassionate, plant-based way of eating was not only best for my fellow sentient beings and for Mother Earth, but also for my personal, spiritual evolution. I choose now to live and act for those with no voice of their own. I want to live congruently with my values and experience spiritual interconnectedness with the world around me, free from an industry of pain and torture.

Whether your perspective is rational, for health reasons, or ethical and spiritual or both, it simply makes sense to be vegan. Veganism is not a religion, a diet, a fad, or a cult; it is simply a path of personal choices and growth, a path of making a mindful and conscious decision to live in a way where all your actions are in alignment with your core values. Every day, you have the power to make these choices, to look out at the world and the predominance of harm and violence and take a stand against it, to look an animal in the eye and see awareness, a life looking back at you, to feel empathy and compassion and care and say, "I will no longer be a part of needless killing." It's a choice—one choice that can make all the difference. Choose it with me. Lettuce live better.

BIBLIOGRAPHY

Inspiring Films, Lectures, and Talks

There is plenty of inspiring content out there if you want to learn more about the benefits of going vegan and about the impact of our diet on our health, and our planet and its resources. I am sharing the list of films and talks that inspired me along my journey for you to check out. You may find a lot out there. Every year, new documentaries and new books come out, so stay on the lookout, and embrace them all with an open mind. Happy exploring!

Films

Health and the Industry

Fat, Sick and Nearly Dead: Follows the story of Australian Joe Cross as he embarks on a journey to regain his health by going on a juice fast and adopting a plant-based diet. He reportedly lost one hundred pounds and was able to safely stop taking his medication.

Food, Inc.: Takes an intimate look at how our food consumption has changed over the past fifty years and how the meat industry is adopting more and more questionable methods to supply demand.

Forks Over Knives: Takes a look at the link between the obesity epidemic and the meat industry as well as how the unhealthy lifestyles of Americans, which cost the country $120 billion a year, can be affected by a change in diet—cutting meat and dairy from our diets and focusing on plant-based foods.

The Game Changers: Focuses on the athletic power of a plant-based diet and challenges "the world's most dangerous myth: that meat is necessary for protein." Features several athletes like Lewis Hamilton, Arnold Schwarzenegger, and strongman Patrik Baboumian and shows the impact plant-based foods has had on their performance.

Supersize Me: Underlines the health risks of excessive fast-food consumption by following filmmaker Morgan Spurlock's thirty-day challenge, during which he ate only McDonald's.

What the Health: Explores the health benefits of a plant-based diet and exposes the shadowy operations in the food industry and the reluctance of health and nutrition organizations to point out the negative effects of consuming animal products.

Empathy and the Animals

Called to Rescue: Explores the tireless work of sanctuary volunteers and staff, the dedication needed for rescue and rehabilitation, and the stories of the animals themselves, living out peaceful lives in sanctuaries.

The Cove: Academy Award-winning film told through Ric O'Barry, a dolphin trainer-turned-activist, aiming to expose the brutal practice of capturing and killing dolphins, a well-kept secret of many local fishermen in Taiji, Japan.

Dominion: With hidden cameras and aerial drones, *Dominion* takes the animal cruelty found in the food system under the spotlight for all to see.

Earthlings: Narrated by Joaquin Phoenix, focuses on the way animals are manipulated by humans for use as food, clothing, entertainment, scientific research and as pets.

Live and Let Live: Does not focus on the reasons to go vegan but instead follows the people who are going vegan, including former butchers and meat factory workers.

Meet Your Meat: Narrated by actor and activist Alec Baldwin, unveils the truth behind "humanity's cruelest invention—the factory farm."

Okja: Tells the story of an unlikely friendship between a young girl and an adorable "super pig" by the name of Okja.

A Prayer for Compassion: Looks at the spirituality involved in living a plant-based, cruelty-free lifestyle. A religious and spiritual awakening to welcome nonhuman animals into your "circle of respect and caring and love."

The Planet

Before the Flood: Actor and environmentalist Leonardo DiCaprio meets activists, scientists, and world leaders to discuss what climate change is doing to our planet and the various ways we could remedy this, acknowledging the hard-to-ignore link between animal agriculture and environmental devastation.

Cowspiracy: Explores the negative impact agricultural farming has on the environment.

Seaspiracy: A filmmaker who is passionate about the ocean sets out to document the impact of fishing on marine species and the environment, and uncovers alarming global corruption along the way.

Short Talks

Best Speech You Will Ever Hear (YouTube/Talk): Gary Yourofsky delivers an inspiring talk to blow away the myths, share interesting facts, and help a group of students make ethical choices for a healthy heart and soul. https://www.youtube.com/watch?v=es6U00LMmC4&has_verified=1

The Food Matrix—101 Reasons to Go Vegan (YouTube/Talk): James Wildman's fascinating and entertaining presentation on the ethical solutions and health benefits of veganism. https://www.youtube.com/watch?v=YnQb58BoBQw

Every Argument Against Veganism (YouTube/TED Talk): Earthling Ed, a vegan educator, debunks every argument against veganism. https://www.youtube.com/watch?v=byTxzzztRBU

How Vegans Can Create Healthy Relationships and Communicate Effectively (YouTube/Talk): Dr. Melanie Joy, psychologist, international speaker, organizational consultant, trainer, and the author of *Why We Love Dogs, Eat Pigs, and Wear Cows* and *Strategic Action for Animals*, helps vegans who find that it's difficult to feel connected with the nonvegans in their lives and to communicate about veganism in a way that doesn't cause conflict. https://www.youtube.com/watch?v=RVnGqibEWVQ&t=2198s

This Speech Will Change Your Life (YouTube/Talk): James Aspey delivers the speech that changed many lives, shedding light on what we are doing to this planet, ourselves, and our fellow earthlings, challenging what most people consider to be "normal." https://www.youtube.com/watch?v=7BCIvrBZ1iQ

You Will Never Look at Your Life in the Same Way Again: Eye-Opening Speech! (YouTube/Talk): Earthling Ed's eye-opening speech that was given to thousands of students in universities across the United Kingdom. https://www.youtube.com/watch?v=Z3u7hXpOm58

The Science Behind the Facts

All nutritional data: https://fdc.nal.usda.gov/

Food choices environmental impact: https://science.sciencemag.org/content/360/6392/987.long

Leading causes of death: https://www.cdc.gov/nchs/fastats/leading-causes-of-death.htm

Vegan calculator: https://www.epa.gov/energy/greenhouse-gas-equivalencies-calculator

Anatomy of humans: Milton R. Mills. "The Comparative Anatomy of Eating." http://www.adaptt.org/documents/Mills%20The%20Comparative%20 Anatomy%20of%20Eating1.pdf

Antibiotic resistance: https://www.ncbi.nlm.nih.gov/pmc/articles/ PMC6760505/. Antimicrobial resistance. (April 2015). Available at: http://www.who.int/mediacentre/factsheets/fs194/en. Accessed September 14, 2015.

Antibiotic sales: https://www.ncbi.nlm.nih.gov/pmc/articles/PMC46 38249/

The China study: https://nutritionstudies.org/the-china-study/.

Campbell, T. C., & Campbell, T. M. (2006). *The China Study: The most comprehensive study of nutrition ever conducted and the startling implications for diet, weight loss and long-term health.*

Dietary animal protein and hip fracture: Abelow, B. J., Holford, T. R, & Insogna, K. L. (1992). "Cross-cultural Association between Dietary Animal Protein and Hip Fracture: A Hypothesis." Calcif Tissue Int 50: 14–8. doi: 10.1007/BF00297291. PMID: 1739864

Dietary protein intake: https://www.ncbi.nlm.nih.gov/pmc/articles/ PMC4081456/, https://www.ncbi.nlm.nih.gov/pmc/articles/PMC68 93534/

Lactose intolerance: https://ghr.nlm.nih.gov/condition/lactose-intolerance#:~:text=Approximately%2065%20percent%20of%20 the,people%20affected%20in%20these%20communities

Micronutrients: https://www.who.int/nutrition/publications/micro nutrients/9241546123/en/ (last accessed October 6, 2006). Report of a Joint Food and Agriculture Organization of the United Nations/ World Food Organization of the United Nations Expert Consultation. *Human Vitamin and Mineral Requirements.* Bangkok, Thailand; September 1998.

Protein overconsumption: https://www.ncbi.nlm.nih.gov/pmc/articles/ PMC4045293/

Impact of milk on planet: https://science.sciencemag.org/content/ 360/6392/987/tab-figures-data

Arguments for veganism and myth busting: https://www.carnismde bunked.com/

Understanding eggs: http://www.makeitpossible.com/guides/egg-labels.php

Link of slaughterhouse working conditions to public health: Cook, E.A.J., de Glanville, W.A., Thomas, L.F. et al. Working Conditions and Public Health Risks in Slaughterhouses in Western Kenya. BMC Public Health 17, 14 (2017). https://doi.org/10.1186/s12889-016-3923-y

ABOUT THE AUTHOR

After experiencing life-changing results by making simple changes, Assile Beydoun wanted to share her story to help others understand the importance of going vegan, physically, mentally, and spiritually. After she received a certification in plant-based nutrition from eCornell and T. Colin Campbell Center for Nutrition Studies, she founded the Dubai Vegan Community, a platform that helps people on their journeys by spreading awareness about the benefits of a plant-based diet, advocating the animal rights movement, promoting sustainable food choices, and breaking stereotypes about veganism. In addition to being the sustainability communications director of a *Fortune* 500 company, Assile also cofounded Spread the Raw, a plant-based snacks distribution company; Wholesome Retreats, for spiritual and wellness retreats; and Cold Pressed, a juice detox program.